HOW 4 FEET OF
PLYWOOD
SAVED THE
GRAND
CANYON

Cover images: Background: *Wood*, courtesy iStockPhoto.com. Back cover clockwise from top left: *Collapse of Teton Dam*, courtesy of U.S. Bureau of Reclamation. *Lee de Forest with Audion Tube*, courtesy of www.Wikimedia.org. *Halifax Explosion*, courtesy of www.Wikimedia.org. *Glen Canyon Dam Overflow Tunnel*, courtesy of U.S. Bureau of Reclamation. *Dr. Amar G. Bose*, Photo courtesy of http://blog.ifitestde/special-50-jahre- hifi/50-jahre-hifi-bose/

Photos in the articles "How Four Feet of Plywood Saved the Grand Canyon" and "Collapse of the Teton Dam" are in the public domain and are used with permission of the United States Department of the Interior, Bureau of Reclamation.

All other photos in the book have separate credits that accompany their placement.

Cover design and interior design by Mark Sonreson, copyright © 2016 by Covenant Communications, Inc.

Published by Covenant Communications, Inc.

American Fork, Utah

Printed in the United States of America

First Printing: May 2016

22 21 20 19 18 17 16   10 9 8 7 6 5 4 3 2 1

ISBN-13: 978-1-52440-028-6

HOW 4 FEET OF PLYWOOD SAVED THE GRAND CANYON

AND 7 OTHER LITTLE-KNOWN INSPIRING TRUE STORIES FROM AMERICAN HISTORY

JERRY BORROWMAN

OTHER BOOKS BY JERRY BORROWMAN

Three Against Hitler
with Rudi Wobbe

A Distant Prayer
with Joseph Banks

Beyond the Call of Duty
with Colonel Bernard Fisher, USAF

'Til the Boys Come Home

I'll Be Seeing You

As Time Goes By

Home Again at Last

One Last Chance

Life & Death at Hoover Dam

Attack the Lusitania

Stories from the Life of Porter Rockwell
with John W. Rockwell

Steamship to Zion

Please visit www.jerryborrowman.com for sample chapters, reviews, and synopses.

ACKNOWLEDGMENTS

I'd like to thank Suellen Riffkin for professionally editing this manuscript, and Geneva Borrowman, my ninety-eight-year-old mother, for proofreading. Norm Jenson and Dave Borrowman provided encouragement and suggestions for the stories. A number of chapters were enriched by live interviews, which are acknowledged within the specific stories. I appreciate the time these contributors donated and the firsthand insights they shared. I particularly want to thank my wife, Marcella, for her adventuresome spirit in traveling with me to so many interesting places.

TABLE OF CONTENTS

Collapse of the Teton Dam

PREFACE

History turns on small points. This book starts with a tragic tale of the world's most catastrophic game of chicken and ends with the nail-biting success story at the Glen Canyon Dam on the Colorado River. Tucked between these bookends are vacuum tubes, ocean-faring steam-ships, inland river steamboats, railroad trains, and the collapse of the Teton Dam. There's even a look at the Yellowstone Supervolcano, which is now 20,000 years overdue for an eruption.

As one who loves history, I have coauthored four autobiographies with American heroes from nineteenth-century America, World War II, and the Vietnam War. I've also written nine books of historical fiction, including military fiction and stories from the Great Depression.

This book, however, takes a different approach from my earlier books. I've selected eight true stories out of American history that I find inspiring but are little known to the general public. Each has affected many lives and deserves wider appreciation. In some cases, I have a personal connection to the story. As a fellow history lover, perhaps you do as well.

—Jerry Borrowman

PHOTO OF HALIFAX EXPLOSION TAKEN APPROXIMATELY 20 SECONDS AFTER THE
BLAST, FROM 13 MILES OUT AT SEA

CHAPTER 1

THE HALIFAX EXPLOSION AND THE BOSTON CHRISTMAS TREE

According to a Mobil Oil advertisement in *Life* magazine,[1] there were only two cars in the entire state of Ohio in the year 1895—and they crashed into each other.[2] The two drivers were confused about who should yield the right of way, neither one conceding until it was too late.

Rather unbelievably, the same thing occurred on a far more tragic scale on the morning of December 6, 1917, in Halifax Harbor in Nova Scotia, Canada. But this confrontation involved a French ammunition ship, *Mont-Blanc*, fully loaded with highly explosive chemicals, and the Belgian Relief Commission freighter *Imo*.

Imo was on the wrong side of the Narrows as it proceeded from the inner harbor toward the sea, forced there by a series of events farther up the channel. But *Mont-Blanc* had ample warning of the *Imo's* position and stubbornly refused to yield its preferred position, even when *Imo* signaled a clear intention to stay on her current path. Only when it became apparent that the two ships were going to collide did the pilots finally take emergency evasive action. But by then it was too late, and both crews watched helplessly as these last-minute actions only compounded the tragedy.

And what a tragedy it was; the resulting explosion was the largest human-caused blast, measured by displacement, in history until the detonation of the atomic bomb over Hiroshima in 1945. The Halifax explosion

---

1. *Life Magazine.* November 24, 1967.
2. Mobil used this ad to discuss ways to decrease the appalling number of traffic accidents in the United States (13 million in 1966) and traffic fatalities (53,000).

was so powerful it obliterated every single structure in the Richmond area of Halifax, killing 2,000 people and injuring 9,000 more.

In addition to instantly destroying more than 1,200 buildings in the Richmond area, the force of the concussion created a seismic wave that shook the ground more than 180 miles from Halifax. Windows shattered in Truro, sixty miles from the blast site. Ships at sea more than eighteen miles from the site felt the powerful shock wave the explosive expansion of the chemicals generated. One of those ships at sea was captained by W.M.A. Campbell, who used his sextant to measure the size of the column of smoke rising from the harbor. It eventually reached more than 12,000 feet (two miles)! Cambell noted that two "angry-looking flames of fire" initially shot up even higher than the cloud of smoke itself.[3]

The noise of the blast was astonishing. Some survivors reported that it immediately overwhelmed their ears, followed by eery silence. This silence was likely the result of all the available air being sucked up by the blast, leaving a vacuum through which sound couldn't travel. But on the outer edge of the shock wave, the explosion created a concussion loud

---

3.   *Explosion in Halifax Harbor.* Flemming, David B. 2004. Formac Publishing Limited, Halifax, Nova Scotia, 36.

HALIFAX EXPLOSION AFTERMATH

enough to be heard in North Cape Breton, more than 220 miles to the east! Canadian Prime Minister Robert Borden heard it in Charlottetown, on Prince Edward Island, 120 miles to the north. When he learned the cause of the noise, he made his way to Halifax to help organize relief efforts.[4]

Perhaps the most incredible aspect of the explosion was that divers in the harbor reported that they saw all the water in the basin entirely displaced by the shock wave's force. Like the biblical parting of the Red Sea, the floor briefly turned into dry land, the water vaporizing or being forced aside by a preventable accident.[5] The tsunami type of wave the blast created washed up on the Dartmouth side of the channel, where it drowned people and destroyed any buildings that had survived the explosion.

The human suffering was unimaginable: hearing loss, broken bones, burns, and blindness from shattered glass. More than 600 people were partially or fully blinded. They had stopped to watch the fire on board the ship down in the harbor, but when the flames on the *Mont-Blanc* reached the TNT, the blast shattered the glass in the windows these people were standing behind, sending shards into their unprotected eyes, faces, and bodies. Many suffered pain and impaired vision for the rest of their lives, and thirty-eight lost their sight permanently.

The tragedy was compounded the next day when the worst blizzard of the season blanketed the devastated area with more than a foot of heavy snow. The streets turned to mud, and relief efforts were stymied. Victims who survived the blast under piles of rubble were doomed to perish in the cold because rescuers couldn't reach them in time.

Even though the account of the Halifax Harbor explosion is fairly obscure today, it is a story of both human folly and incredible human resilience. It brought out the very best in the rescuers who rushed to the scene, including a large contingent of doctors and medical personnel from Boston, Massachusetts, whose sacrifice earned the enduring gratitude of the residents of Halifax. The bond that formed between Boston and Halifax is now memorialized each year by the gift of a stately Christmas tree the Haligonians (residents of Halifax) send to the citizens of Boston. In tribute,

4.   *Shattered City: The Halifax Explosion and the Road to Recovery.* Kitz, Janet. 1989. Nimbus Publishing. ISBN 978-0-921054-30-6.

5.   Op cit, 36.

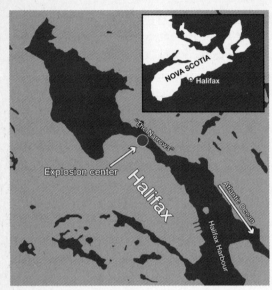

MAP OF HALIFAX HARBOR, NOVA SCOTIA, CANADA; NOTE THE HOUR GLASS SHAPE THAT FORMS AN UPPER AND LOWER HARBOR

the Bostonians display the tree on Prudential Square as a memorial to that bitter December day in 1917.

BOSTON AND HALIFAX

As one of the world's great naturally ice-free harbors, Halifax is strategically located on the Great Circle Route that carries maritime traffic between the United States, Great Britain, and Europe. Without a major river feeding into it and shaped like a giant hourglass, the inner harbor at the top of the hourglass is virtually wave free and ice free all months of the year. These unique conditions make it an ideal stopping-off point for ships bound to or from Europe.

In December 1917, more than forty ships were moored in both areas of the harbor, and other ships waited outside the antisubmarine nets placed at the entrance to the outer harbor for permission to enter.

Among the ships waiting was the *Mont-Blanc*, which had arrived the night before after a four-day journey from New York City. With the First World War raging in France, the munitions the ship carried were urgently needed by the Allies, but *Mont-Blanc* had to replenish her coal bunkers before launching out into the Atlantic.

Relations were positive between the U.S. and Canada—we were allies in the war—but this hadn't always been the case. In 1776 and 1812, Halifax had been the perfect staging ground for British warships and troopships as they had prepared to invade American ports to the south. During those war years, Halifax-based privateers captured many New England ships and sold them as prizes.

From the Canadians' point-of-view, the War of 1812 was a war of aggression on the part of the United States. While the primary conflict of the War of 1812 was America versus England, the U.S. government used it as an excuse to invade Canada. Because many battles raged on Canadian soil, the Canadians felt that America was seeking to annex Canada into the United States. They fiercely rejected this and even launched a military strike force from Halifax into Maine in September 1814. By the end of this battle, the Canadians held much of the Maine coast. In fact, Maine was only returned to the United States when the Peace Treaty of Ghent, signed on December 24, 1814, ended the war.

Canadians view their successful repulse of American incursions in 1812 as significant victories, contributing to their national identity that separated them from their more populous neighbors to the south.[6]

So, in December 1917 when the explosion occurred, the Haligonians and New Englanders recognized that their mutual trade route profited them both, but they did not share a humanitarian bond. That would very soon change.

THE COLLISION

At 7:15 a.m. on December 6, 1917, shortly after the opening of the submarine nets, the *Mont-Blanc* received permission from the Halifax Harbor Authority to proceed north into the outer harbor. Under the command of Captain Aime Le Medec, Francis Mackey, a local pilot, provided direction as the *Mont-Blanc* started into the channel at approximately 7:30 a.m. The *Mont-Blanc* was a large ship for its day, displacing 3,121 gross tons and measuring 345 feet in length by 44.8 feet in the beam. Fully loaded with cargo, the ship rode low in the water.

The path *Mont-Blanc* was supposed to follow required her to keep to the starboard side of the channel.[7] (Starboard is the right side of the ship when looking forward.) That meant *Mont-Blanc* should stay on the Dartmouth side of the Narrows (the slender neck of water between the upper and lower harbors where the passage narrowed to less than half a mile).

These rules of the road also meant that ships coming out of the upper port needed to stay to the Richmond-Halifax side on their starboard. Stated

---

6.   *War of 1812.* The Canadian Encyclopedia. Article by James H. Marsh, Pierre Berton, revised by Tabitha Marshall. Published 03/06/2012. Last Edited 03/20/2015. www.canadianencylopedia.ca/en/m/article/war-of-1812/.

7.   This requirement was in effect by terms of the "International Rules of the Road, Regulations for Preventing Collisions at Sea," (1910).

another way, ships were supposed to pass each other "port-to-port." It was with this understanding that *Mont-Blanc* started into the Narrows, correctly positioned.

The *Imo* was a larger cargo ship, displacing 5,043 gross tons and sizing out at 430 feet in length and 45 feet in breadth. Under charter to the Belgian Relief Commission, she had arrived in Halifax from Rotterdam on December 3 while en route to New York City to pick up relief supplies.

Without any cargo, *Imo* rode high in the water and had spent the nights of December 3 and 4 in the inner harbor. Although the *Imo* had been cleared to leave port the evening of December 5, the refueling ship arrived too late to load coal onto it in time for it to depart before the submarine nets closed. They did, however, complete the refueling operation that evening.

The next morning, at approximately eight o'clock, *Imo* Captain Hakkon From impatiently ordered the ship out of its berth to start the passage down through the Narrows. However, Captain From's order to proceed exceeded his authority since Harbor Control had not renewed its permission granted the previous evening for *Imo* to proceed. In addition to that critical procedural error, the ship continued into the passage at over seven knots per hour, which was much faster than the prescribed speed. In these unusually risky maneuvers, the ship was under the guidance of a local pilot, William Hayes.

With the stage set, the disaster began to unfold. After maneuvering between numerous vessels in the upper harbor, the *Imo* started swinging to starboard (the Richmond-Halifax side) as it entered the Narrows. It was then that Pilot Hayes saw that the American steamer *Clara* was heading north through the channel on the wrong side, i.e. the *Clara's* port side. Pilot Hayes ordered Captain From to give two short blasts of *Imo's* steam whistle to indicate that he would allow the *Clara* to maintain its present course. This decision forced *Imo* to the center of the channel rather than to the starboard side near Richmond-Halifax. Simultaneously the tugboat *Stella Maris* pulled away from Pier 8 on the Halifax side with two barges in tow. This forced the *Imo* even closer to the Dartmouth side. *Imo* was now way out of the prescribed course but had communicated—by blasts of her horn—with the other ships involved in order to pass them safely.

It was about this time that the pilot of the *Mont-Blanc* noticed the large *Imo* to his north on the wrong side of the channel. Since *Mont-Blanc* was well into the Narrows, Pilot Mackey ordered Captain Le Medec to give one short blast of the ship's whistle to indicate his intention to move even closer to the starboard shore. His expectation was that *Imo* would move to her correct position in the lane on *Imo's* starboard side, near Halifax. To provide room for *Imo* to maneuver, Mackey slowed *Mont-Blanc*.

But instead of complying with this signal, *Imo's* Pilot Hayes sounded two short blasts of the *Imo's* whistle indicating that he intended to hold his course on the Dartmouth side of the channel. In other words, he felt the best way for the ships to pass each other was for the *Mont-Blanc* to move to the left (port) as the other ships had done. His motivation in doing so was to allow the tugboat *Stella Maris* to keep to her path going into the upper basin.

Well, what to do? Mackey, who was unaware of the *Stella Maris*, signaled a second time to confirm his commitment to the starboard approach to the channel, and he kept the *Mont-Blanc* close to the Dartmouth shore. Hayes responded with two more blasts, insisting that *he* was holding to the Dartmouth shore. The two ships were now on a direct collision course with rapidly diminishing room to maneuver. Finally, sensing disaster, Pilot Mackey decided to give way and ordered the *Mont-Blanc* to turn to port so the ships would pass starboard-to-starboard. At almost the same moment, Pilot Hayes gave three blasts on *Imo's* whistle to indicate he was putting his engines in reverse to avoid the collision. Because the *Imo* was riding high in the water, it took longer than usual for the propellers to slow the ship. And because the torque of the reversal actually swung the bow of the ship to starboard, the two ships were now moving in exactly the same area of the channel. With no more room to maneuver, the forward momentum of both ships made a collision inevitable. The *Imo* crashed into the starboard side of the *Mont-Blanc* at almost a right angle, cutting a six-foot gash in the *Mont-Blanc's* hull.[8]

8.   Flemming, David B. *Explosion in Halifax Harbor*. 2004. Formac Publishing Limited, Halifax, Nova Scotia, 24–25. The source for this sequence of events, repeated in numerous sources, came from official inquiries at the time as presented by Captain Le Medic and Pilot Mackey. Mr. Flemming notes in E*xplosion in Halifax Harbor* that the pilot of the *Imo*, Johan Johansen (the only survivor of the *Imo's* bridge party) disputed this version of events, indicating that *Imo* was much closer to midchannel than claimed by the *Mont-Blanc* party and that his pilot had signaled an intention to move to the starboard (Halifax) side of the channel, only altering course when the *Mont-Blanc* also turned toward that side of the channel. He also stated the *Imo's* original two-whistles was directed at the tugboat, not the *Mont-Blanc*. Of such misunderstandings do tragedies arise.

Because both ships were in reverse, the wound itself was not particularly significant and would not have threatened the *Mont-Blanc* under normal circumstances, but the friction of metal-on-metal where the two ships crashed sparked some of the picric acids stored in barrels on the *Mont-Blanc* deck. As fire from this acid spread toward ruptured barrels of the highly flammable accelerant benzene, Captain Le Medec and Pilot Mackey knew a colossal explosion was inevitable. There was simply no way they could get the fires put out in time to prevent them from reaching the TNT down in the hold. Accordingly Le Medec ordered his men to abandon ship, and as they did so, they shouted out to other ships nearby that the ship was going to explode. But their cries could not be heard through the commotion.[9]

HEROISM IN THE FACE OF MORTAL DANGER

Not realizing the full extent of the danger, some ships in the area made their way toward the *Mont-Blanc* to try to extinguish the fires. Eight men from HMCS *Niobe* approached the burning ship to pull it back into the Narrows from the Halifax Pier 6, into which it had drifted. These men hoped to prevent the burning ship from setting the piers on fire. Unfortunately they had no way of knowing the hold was loaded with explosives.

Meanwhile, in a small railway telegraph office in the center of the wharf, near the Narrows, signalman Vincent Coleman was startled by a sound out in the harbor. Looking up from his equipment, he saw dark billows of smoke rising near Pier 6. Just then a sailor burst into the room shouting that the *Mont-Blanc*, an ammunition ship, was on fire in the harbor and was likely to explode. The sailor urged everyone to leave as quickly as possible. Coleman got up and left the building with the others but then turned around to go back. He was worried about a passenger train that was inbound to Halifax and was on schedule to pass right by where the *Mont-Blanc* was on fire. With full knowledge of the danger, he frantically typed out a warning to the approaching train that was recorded as follows: *"Hold up the train. Ammunition ship afire in harbor making for Pier 6 and will explode. Guess this will be my last message. Goodbye, boys."*[10]

9.   Later, well after the explosion, they were accused of cowardice for not staying on board and striving to extinguish the flames before the horrible explosion that followed.

10.   Nova Scotia Museum, Department of Tourism and Culture. http://maritimemuseum.novascotia.ca/what-see-do/halifax-explosion/vincent-coleman-and-halifax-explosion.

Coleman did not survive the blast, but his sacrifice was not in vain. The passenger train he signaled responded to the warning and stopped outside the blast area, very likely saving the lives of all on board.

Sailors who were not aware of the volatile cargo on *Mont-Blanc* were attempting to attach a hawser line to the burning ship so they could tow it back into the channel. That was when the explosion occurred. It was 9:35 a.m. So intense was the fireball of the explosion that the ship's metal superstructure instantly vaporized. Pieces of the thick steel hull blew almost 1,000 feet into the air. The best summary I've found of what happened next comes from Laura M. Mac Donald's book *Curse of the Narrows*:

> Altogether 2,925 tons or 5.85 million pounds of powder exploded, giving off over 9,000 degrees Fahrenheit heat. All, 6,880,627 pounds of the *Mont-Blanc's* iron hull shot up over a thousand feet, roiling within the initial flame ball until much of it vaporized. The anchor snapped its chain and separated, sending the 1,140-pound shank whirling through the skies over Richmond Hill and across the city for 2.35 miles. It landed on the other side of the peninsula of Halifax across the Northwest Arm. The aft cannon shot off the stern and arced over the harbor and Dartmouth's North End for three miles, landing next to a small lake. As the cloud lifted and cooled in the clean air, white-hot fragments of the *Mont-Blanc* showered down across the streets of Halifax-Dartmouth. What was left of the boiling benzol rose into the air with the cloud and combined with the carbon particles given off by the explosives to create a slick black rain that fell across parts of both cities for as long as ten minutes.

> On land, the sound arrived first. It rippled through the earth at the punishing speed of 13,320 miles per hour—twenty-three times the speed of sound. Depending on how far away people were, survivors perceived it as a rumble or a boom. Those who were close, such as the Mi'kmaq at Turtle Grove, described it as a buzzing sound. . . .

> Some people reported hearing two blasts, but what they actually heard was the air catching up to the sound. "The concussion went right in you, like right in, you could feel it. You could feel it! Blowing!" Others, such as Jean Lindsay at the Dalhousie library or Pharmacist Bertha Archibald in the South End, heard a noise ten seconds before the windows shattered.

HALIFAX AFTER THE HALIFAX EXPLOSION, LOOKING TOWARD THE DARTMOUTH SIDE OF THE HARBOUR, 1917

In Dartmouth, some people counted forty seconds. . . .

The air blast blew through the narrow streets, toppling buildings and crashing through windows, doors, walls, and chimneys until it slowed to 756 miles an hour, 5 miles below the speed of sound. The blast crushed internal organs, exploding lungs and eardrums of those standing closest to the ship, most of whom died instantly. It picked up others, only to thrash them against trees, walls, and lampposts with enough force to kill them. Roofs and ceilings collapsed on top of their owners. Floors dropped into the basement and trapped families under timber, beams, and furniture. This was particularly dangerous for those close to the harbor because a fireball, which was invisible in the daylight, shot out over a one-to-four-mile area surrounding the *Mont-Blanc*. Richmond houses caught fire like so much kindling. In houses able to withstand the blast, windows stretched inward until the glass shattered around its weakest point, sending out a shower of arrow-shaped slivers that cut their way through curtains, wallpaper, and walls. The glass spared no one. Some people were beheaded where they stood; others were saved by a falling bed or bookshelf. It pierced the face and upper chests of anyone unlucky enough to still be standing in front of a window.

In the harbor, the heat of the explosion was so intense that a twenty-foot radius of water around the Mont-Blanc instantly evaporated. As the air pressure pushing outward from the ship diminished, water from all over the harbor rushed into the void. The volume was so great that it sucked the water from other shores until men as far away as the dry dock and Tuft's Cover were shocked to see the harbor floor exposed. As the waves surged back toward Pier 6, they collided with such force that a geyser shot out of the harbor up into the sky. The higher it rose, the more water it pulled from the opposite shores. When the geyser finally collapsed under its own weight, this sudden addition of water destabilized the harbor . . . and a semicircular tsunami rippled outward across the harbor, picking up more water and force until it was twenty feet high. The wall of water picked up bits of metal, swept men off decks, broke mooring lines, and spit ships aside as it sped outward to the Basin and the sea.[11]

At a force of 3 kilotons of TNT, the *Mont-Blanc* became the largest bomb in the history of the world, the hull of the ship creating the containment vessel required for the explosion. In a matter of mere moments, the *Mont-Blanc* simply ceased to exist. Other ships were tossed up and out of the harbor by the force of the blast. Some were thrown by the tsunami wave and deposited on the Richmond or Halifax side, depending on where they were at the time of the explosion.

Survivors of this blast described what happened to them differently: some said they heard a deafening blast, followed by incredible pressure against the side of their body facing the harbor. Others said everything went completely silent. Virtually everyone who lived through it felt it was a cataclysm of unimaginable fury.

Perhaps geography was the only mitigating force in the story. For as terrible as it was, the consequences of the blast would have been even worse if not for the fact that the harbor was in a bowl ringed with hills. While the bowl itself was a death trap, the upward slope of the hills directed the blast out from the center and up toward the sky, sparing many buildings and people on the opposite sides of the hills.

---

11. *Curse of the Narrows*. Mac Donald, Laura M. Walker Publishing Company, Inc., New York, 2005. 62–66.

LOOKING NORTH TOWARD PIER 8 FROM HILLIS FOUNDRY AFTER GREAT EXPLOSION, HALIFAX, DEC. 6, 1917

RUMORS AND A BLIZZARD

With so many dead and injured people, survivors outside the blast area did their best to regain their wits and rush to the site of the explosion to render assistance. Volunteer firefighters, neighbors, and family members struggled through the debris into the blast zone and saved many lives through their heroic efforts. Because the exact cause of the blast was unknown, rumors started flying that it was the result of saboteurs from Germany, who were even then working to cause additional destruction. When smoke from a fire was spotted near an armory on the Dartmouth side of the channel, someone predicted that another blast was coming, and orders were given to retreat from the area. This action deprived many injured survivors of the help they needed in those crucial early moments and probably led to even more deaths. The rumor regarding another blast was unfounded since the subsequent fire resulted from the heat blast of

the original explosion, but how could anyone know what else was coming? People look for a rationale at such times. The thought that the cause of this horror was nothing more than miscommunication between two ships in the harbor gave no meaning at all to the suffering of the victims.

In spite of the lack of communication within the blast area, government officials in Halifax did their best to organize relief efforts. Area hospitals started receiving the injured. As word of the explosion reached other cities by telegraph and telephone, people throughout Eastern Canada and the New England area of the United States stopped what they were doing to figure out how they could help. But those efforts would take time. In Halifax, snow started falling—soon to turn into the worst blizzard in memory. The drifting snow quickly covered the grimy black film that had rained down from the skies, and the howling wind made it difficult to hear the cries of the injured. It also led to additional deaths from hypothermia as those trapped in wreckage slowly froze to death. The blizzard froze the hands, arms, and faces of those who were trying to render assistance.. It is impossible to imagine the misery of the people trapped in this unyielding nightmare.

BOSTON SENDS RELIEF

The State of Massachusetts in conjunction with the American Red Cross created the Halifax-Massachusetts Relief Committee to help the relief efforts in Halifax. A train was dispatched from Boston late in the evening on December 7, just one day after the explosion, carrying enough supplies to stock a temporary relief hospital. On board were twelve surgeons and ten nurses, who quickly deployed upon their arrival in Halifax. In time, others joined them from New York, Philadelphia, Rhode Island, Washington, Montreal, and Toronto. While the local doctors had done remarkably well in responding in the first crucial hours, by Monday they were exhausted and welcomed assistance from outside. A second Boston train arrived on December 9, establishing a hospital at St. Mary's College.

These early relief efforts were critical in saving lives and alleviating suffering. But because the effects of the devastation required decades of rebuilding, the Halifax-Massachusetts Relief Committee continued to render aid for many years beyond the immediate crisis. Groundbreaking research helped many of those who were blinded by shattered glass, returning sight to some and providing long-term assistance to those permanently blinded. Cash donations were made to help rebuild the city, including building medical facilities and helping furnish new homes built to replace those destroyed. In total, the Halifax-Massachusetts Relief Committee raised $716,000 (in 1917 dollars) to assist those whose lives were disrupted by the tragedy.[12]

INVESTIGATION

Within days of the disaster, an investigation convened before the Wreck Commissioner's Court to determine the root of the tragedy and to assign responsibility to those who had caused it. Some assigned blame to the Norwegian crew of the *Imo* for no other reason than that they were in the midst of World War I and their language sounded like German. Others in the community blamed the crew of the *Mont-Blanc* for abandoning the ship without trying to extinguish the fires and without giving more warning of the impending explosion. Survivors of both crews were placed under police protection because of death threats.

12. Ibid.

At the conclusion of the hearing, the administrative judge assigned sole blame for the accident to Captain Le Medec of the *Mont-Blanc* and Francis Mackey, the pilot. In a subsequent action, they were arrested for manslaughter in the deaths of the pilot and captain of the *Imo*, but these charges were later dropped.

When the owners of the two ships sued each other for damages, the court again held that it was Le Medec who was responsible. But on the appeal of this decision to the Supreme Court of Canada, blame was assigned equally to the officers of both ships. For the rest of his life, Pilot Mackey held that *Imo* was at fault since she left her anchorage without renewed permission from the port authority. Johan Johansen, the helmsman of the *Imo* and the only survivor of the bridge party, contended they were in the correct channel. He stated that they reversed engines only when the *Mont-Blanc* turned toward the Halifax side of the harbor, which made the collision inevitable. In the end, it didn't matter who was responsible since the damage was done and was irreversible. The cost in lives and human suffering was too great to be compensated for monetarily.

The Nova Scotia Christmas Tree at Boston Common

The remarkable thing about the Halifax-Massachusetts Relief Committee was that it continued to provide assistance to Halifax for decades—long after the initial crisis was over. One year after the tragedy, in December 1918, the citizens of Halifax sent a large, freshly cut Christmas tree to the City of Boston as an expression of their gratitude for all the help given. This large tree was displayed on the Boston Common and helped cement the bond that had grown between the two cities.

This was originally intended as a one-time token of appreciation, but in 1971, members of the Lunenburg County Christmas Tree Producers Association of Nova Scotia read about this earlier gesture and decided to send another tree to rekindle that earlier bond.[13] The gift was so well received that it started an annual tradition that continues to the present, with the government of Nova Scotia eventually assuming responsibility for selecting and sending the tree.

There is a formal ceremony when the tree comes via truck to Halifax, where it is one of the stars in a grand annual Christmas parade. Then it is reloaded for transport to Boston. School children in Canada send the tree off, and school children in Boston are on hand to welcome its arrival.

---

13. It was also a way to promote Christmas tree exports.

The lighting ceremony on Boston Common has become a well-publicized event where a crowd of approximately 20,000 joins with officials from both countries to celebrate the season while honoring the events of 1917.[14]

TOURING HALIFAX AND LEARNING OF THE EXPLOSION

My wife, Marcella, and I first learned of the Halifax explosion while on a "fall leaves" cruise from Boston to Montreal. We scheduled ourselves for a walking tour of Halifax on the day our ship was in port, not knowing anything about the city or its history. A bus took us from the harbor to the base of the Angus L. Macdonald Bridge, a suspension bridge that crosses the southern end of the Halifax Harbor Narrows. It was from this rather lofty perch above the water that we gazed down on the site of the great explosion of December 1917 while our guide told us about the harrowing events of that day. He was able to point to the place where the collision occurred and then describe the incredible damage on both the Halifax and Dartmouth shores. We did this walk on a beautiful fall day in a city pristine with manicured lawns, beautiful hardwood trees with their foliage in fall colors, and spotlessly clean city streets. As we continued across the bridge to the Dartmouth side of the harbor, our guide walked us through the bowl where the great tsunami wave rose from the harbor. He pointed out how this wave finished the work of destruction that started with the explosion, and he concluded with stories of the survivors, the victims, and the heroism of the rescue workers. At the ferry terminal, we observed artifacts and photos. Our tour ended with a ferryboat ride across the Narrows, where, back on the Halifax shore, I made my way to the Maritime Museum to buy some books that gave greater details on the explosion. This experience and my further reading became the inspiration for this article.

It was also on this tour that our guide told us the Canadians' version of the War of 1812. To them, the war was a great victory for their national integrity. Our guide indicated that few of his American guests have any idea that our country attempted to conquer parts of Canada. Those of us in the walking group admitted that it was news to us. Something that mattered a great deal to the Canadians is hardly even a footnote in U.S. history books.

---

14. "Boston Christmas Tree." Wikipedia, the Free Encyclopedia. Wikimedia Foundation, Inc. 19 May 2015. https://en.wikipedia.org/wiki/Boston_Christmas_Tree.

As we expressed remorse for our ignorance, our guide smiled and said that all is forgiven now—1917 erased the animosity. Today it is a Christmas tree that erases the border each and every year.

The Halifax explosion was a disaster without excuse, caused by human stubbornness. That so many innocent people suffered needlessly is a scandal. The depraved indifference of a pilot and captain who failed to exercise caution, even while fully aware of the explosive volatility of their cargo, is impossible to imagine.

And yet, as awful as the Ḥalifax explosion of 1917 was, the next chapter looks at an impending explosion that dwarfs even the most powerful nuclear blasts. It is about a volcanic eruption that will have a negative impact all around the world. In a single day, the effects of thousands of years of global warming will be reversed as the world is plunged into years of perpetual winter. Oh, and the western United States as we know it today will cease to exist. Science fiction? No—it is the Yellowstone Supervolcano that is now 20,000 years overdue to explode . . .

SOURCES

1. *Explosion in Halifax Harbor.* David B. Flemming. 2004. Formac Publishing Limited, Halifax, Nova Scotia.

2. *Curse of the Narrows.* Laura M. Mac Donald. 2005. Walker Publishing Company, Inc., New York.

3. "War of 1812." The Canadian Encyclopedia. Article by James H. Marsh and Pierre Berton, revised by Tabitha Marshall. Published 03/06/2012. Last Edited 03/20/2015. www.canadianencylopedia.ca/en/m/article/war-of-1812/.

4. Vincent Coleman, Nova Scotia Museum, Department of Tourism and Culture. http://maritimemuseum.novascotia.ca/what-see-do'halifax-explosion/vincent-coleman-and-halifaxexplosion.

5. "The Boston Christmas Tree." Wikipedia, the Free Encyclopedia. Wikimedia Foundation, Inc. May 2015. https://en.wikipedia.org/wiki/Boston_Christmas_Tree.

Old Faithful, Yellowstone National Park

CHAPTER 2

THE YELLOWSTONE SUPERVOLCANO

Raise your hand if you've ever visited Yellowstone National Park. If your arm went up, you have been one of the 3 million people who visit the nation's oldest national park each year. And you are one of the more than 60 million who have visited Yellowstone since it was first discovered by white explorers in the late 1870s.

Now raise your hand again if, while you were in the park, you realized you were standing on top of the world's largest active supervolcano! Statistics tell us that not nearly as many people raise their hands for this question. And it's easy to understand why since Yellowstone is actually quite a placid place to visit, with vast open skies and pine forests. It is even relaxing to stand on the boardwalks by Old Faithful as it blasts scalding water up into the sky while releasing the warm scent of sulfur steam. To me, it feels like stepping into a steam room after a good workout. This sense of good-natured serenity is even more evident at the paint pots, which are endlessly bubbling mud fields. Heated steam forces its way to the surface through multicolored layers of sputtering mud in hues of grays, pinks, and blues.

My favorite activity is to gaze into one of the many deep pools, like Morning Glory, where dark indigo water emits wisps of sulfuric steam. Looking into the depths of the multihued pool gives a sense that they are bottomless, that you could dive in and descend forever. But, of course, it would boil you to death if you set foot in one of these pools! Indeed,

Yellowstone is full of wonder, where more than 300 geysers (the most in the world) provide endless variety to tourists who come to see these unusual natural marvels.

There is a reason for all of that thermal activity. It turns out that the Yellowstone Basin is situated on the remains of four overlapping volcanic calderas that measure more than thirty-five miles across, twelve miles long, and forty-five miles deep. A caldera is the sunken remains of a volcanic eruption that expelled so much superheated lava into the air that once the lava was released, the magma chamber of the volcano collapsed on itself. The remnants of the destruction form a large crater, or bowl, in the landscape. The ferocious eruption that took place at Huckleberry Ridge in Yellowstone approximately 2.1 million years ago was so spectacular that it exploded with more than 2,500 times the explosive power of the Mount St. Helens eruption in Washington State in 1980.

In fact, the ancient Huckleberry Ridge eruption at Yellowstone is the most massive volcanic eruption in the geologic record. It was spectacular. But it didn't finish the job. There's still magma brewing in its ancient magma chamber.

ONE OF HUNDREDS OF HOT WATER POOLS IN YELLOWSTONE NATIONAL PARK; SOME ARE BATHTUB WARM, OTHERS ARE BOILING

While the other stories in this book tell of events that have happened, this story is about what will happen. *Will* is the correct word, for geologists are 100 percent confident that Yellowstone will erupt again. The only question is when. Some scientists believe it could happen any day, while others think the amount of molten magma in the chamber under Yellowstone is too small at present to pose any danger of an immediate eruption. Only time will tell, but since geologic time is so far outside our own limited time frames, it's presently impossible to develop any odds regarding another supereruption occurring in our lifetime.

This much we do know: when it does occur, it will be devastating all around the world, producing enough ash to cause at least two or three years of perpetual winter all around the globe. It will destroy crops and lead to the extinction of many fragile species. In the immediate area of Yellowstone, poisonous fumes and explosive uplift will kill everything within fifty to a hundred miles. It is also likely that hundreds of thousands more will die from respiratory distress as the preponderance of ash rains down from the skies as far south as Arizona and as far east as Minneapolis. So this story that is yet to occur is ominous.

So, what are the odds of an eruption in our lifetime? After all, 2.1 million years is a long time ago, which makes the danger of a current eruption seem quite remote. Except that the Mesa Falls eruption on the outer edge of the park occurred 1.3 million years ago, and the Lava Creek eruption at what is now Old Faithful happened 640,000 years ago. Perhaps you discern a pattern here: 640,000 X 2 = 1.3 million; 640,000 X 3 = 1.9 million (really close to 2.1 million). In other words, the pattern is that the Yellowstone volcano erupts approximately every 650,000 to 700,000 years. And it's been roughly that long since it last erupted. Perhaps more threatening is the fact that the ground in Yellowstone Park heaves up and down each and every year, rising by more than a yard in just the past ninety years. It has risen by more than six inches per year in very recent years. In fact, the beautiful Yellowstone Lake has tipped enough from this uplift that trees at the southern end have become inundated with water.

Here's what's going on: Yellowstone Park's magma chamber extrudes up from the depths of the earth to within just three miles of the surface (compared to the crust's average thickness of 25 miles under most continents). According to Greg Breining, in his book *Super Volcano—The Ticking Time*

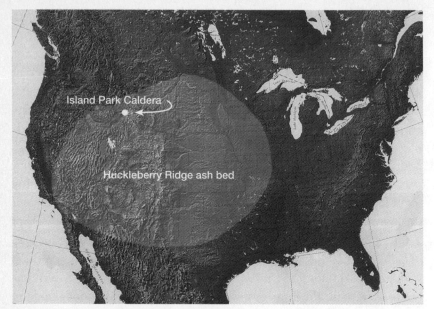

HUCKLEBERRY RIDGE TUFF

Bomb Beneath Yellowstone National Park, the molten magma is contained by the incredible pressure that keeps it in check. But whenever the pressure grows large enough that magma is extruded to the surface, an explosive reaction takes place, the vapor in the magma expanding exponentially after it is freed from the compression and exposed to the open air. In fact, the expansion ratio is more than 670 times! Breining says that at this rate, "a lump of magma the size of an airline carry-on bag would expand to fill your living room."[1]

I like to think of it as exploding popcorn kernels. When locked in its chamber, the magma is contained, as is a popcorn kernel, but when it escapes from the high-pressure dome, it expands in a pattern that can quickly escalate into a full-scale eruption. So great is the explosive power that when the explosion occurred 2.1 million years ago at Huckleberry Ridge, the magma blanketed the entire surface of the United States as far east as the Mississippi River. Even a relatively small eruption in the Yellowstone area some 70,000 years ago threw up enough debris to bury both Hoover Dam and Glen Canyon Dam (if those dams had existed then) when it fell back down to Earth.

---

1. *Super Volcano: The Ticking Time Bomb Beneath Yellowstone National Park.* Greg Breining. Voyageur Press, an imprint of Quarto Publishing Group USA, Inc. Minneapolis MN. 30.

Why is Yellowstone so volatile? It turns out that there is an 18-million-year-old geologic hotspot now centered in Idaho and Wyoming. This hotspot created the Snake River Plain that extends all the way from the Nevada border to the Yukon area in Canada. In a mind-bending illustration of geographic time, this hotspot has stayed in the same place as plate tectonics have moved the crust of the earth above it at a rate of approximately one inch per year. This remarkable hotspot has produced at least a dozen supervolcanos and many hundreds of smaller eruptions and lava flows over the course of millions of years. It has also caused hundreds of thousands of earthquakes, with more than 3,000 in 2014 alone! The Yellowstone supereruptions are just the most recent in this hotspot's series of awe-inspiring activity.

Taking these factors into consideration, Yellowstone is an exceptional area of the world, far more complex than even its geothermal wonders suggest. With its heaving and sighing caldera underfoot, who knows who will be caught when the volcano finally erupts? Perhaps it will be you or me.

PERSONAL CONNECTION

Growing up in Pocatello, Idaho, I considered Yellowstone my figurative backyard. My father loved the place, and our family made the three-hour trip by car to Yellowstone, Grand Teton, and Island Parks (all connected to each other) every single year. I loved exploring the geothermal features of the park, as well as boating on Yellowstone Lake with my favorite cousins, aunts, and uncles. My grandfather Borrowman was a committed fisherman, and he knew all the best streams in both Yellowstone and Island Park.

As a young child, just seven years old in 1960, I remember learning about the Hebgen Lake earthquake on the border of Yellowstone Park. In fact, I was quite disappointed that I'd slept through it since my parents and their friends had been awakened by the trembling. One of my mother's friends, who worked at the Idaho State Hospital South in Blackfoot, said the multistory buildings of the hospital literally swayed from side to side. But being a sound sleeper at the age of seven, I slept through the whole thing.

Once the aftershocks died down, my father couldn't wait to see what had happened, so we drove up to the earthquake area and went exploring. My cousin Mark and I were fascinated by the newly formed Quake Lake that had come into existence because of a natural dam a landslide had formed during the earthquake. We were able to walk on the side walls of a house that had been tipped on its side and was partially submerged by the new lake. It all seemed scary and intriguing at the time. I had no idea earthquakes were actually a common experience in Yellowstone, with this simply being the largest in our lifetime.

Later, as a Boy Scout, I went on a fifty-mile hike with my troop into the Beckler Meadows area just outside the boundaries of Yellowstone in Island Park. We swam in a large, natural warm-springs pool on a cold, rainy morning. I suppose we should have been a little more concerned about our safety, given the pool right next to the one we swam in was hot enough to boil an egg! But we were Scouts, and it was a great adventure.

Finally, when I was an adult, my wife and I moved our family farther south to Salt Lake City, but we still took our kids on vacations to Yellowstone and Teton National Parks. After all, it is a world-class tourist destination just six hours from our home. We hiked up the base of the Grand Teton Mountains at Jenny's Lake. We swam in Jackson Lake by the magnificent Jackson Lake Lodge.

A SMALL GEYSER IN YELLOWSTONE NATIONAL PARK

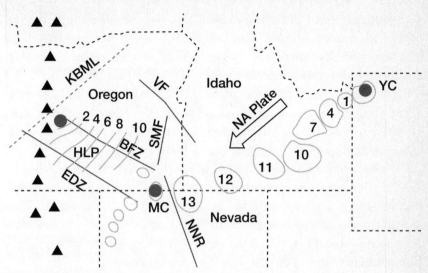

NEWBERRY-YELLOWSTONE TRACKS

This area really is part and parcel of my life. And yet, until just recently, I had no idea Yellowstone Park was anything other than benign. I first learned of the Yellowstone hotspot and the vast underground magma chamber while watching a *History Channel* program on Yellowstone Park. That led to additional research, which then led to this article.

The *History Channel* program taught me that the caldera was not just figuratively my backyard; it quite literally *was* my backyard. Blackfoot, Idaho, where I was born, sits on the Snake River basalt plain, created from lava flows. In fact, it is because of the unique soil conditions of broken-down lava that Blackfoot styles itself as the "Potato Capital of the World." It is in Bingham County (with Blackfoot being the county seat) that the world-famous Idaho potatoes are at their best because the volcanic soil in the area gives the russet potatoes a unique taste and texture. To the west of Blackfoot are three large volcanoes known as the Twin Buttes and the Big Butte. These giant mountains are remnants of the time when Blackfoot sat atop the Yellowstone hotspot before continental drift moved it farther to the southwest. Also to the west is the remarkable Craters of the Moon National Monument, which was created by lava flows as recently as when Columbus was first setting foot in the Americas.

So it turns out the Yellowstone hotspot created the very landscape on which I grew up.

Perhaps I'll end with a story I heard that illustrates the illusive nature of time to creatures who are lucky to make it to even a hundred years old. The story goes that a man was reading the Bible when he came across this passage in Luke: "With the Lord a day is like a thousand years."[2]

As he considered this time frame, he had an idea and said a prayer. "Hey, God, could I have ten thousand dollars?" he asked, figuring that God's math would make him fabulously wealthy. As the story goes, God was in a good mood and replied, "Sure. Just a minute . . ."

So it is with Yellowstone. Some think we are 20,000 years past due for the next eruption, given that 640,000 years have passed. But since 20,000 years is a relative "minute" in geological time, it may very well be that nothing at all will happen in any time frame that matters to us. But then again, perhaps it will. Now enjoy your next visit to Yellowstone, but beware if the soles of your feet start getting warm.

SOURCES

1. "Yellowstone Caldera." Wikipedia, the Free Encyclopedia. https://en.wikipedia.org/wiki/Yellowstone_Caldera. 7/13/2015.

2. *Super Volcano, The Ticking Time Bomb Beneath Yellowstone National Park.* Greg Breining. Voyageur Press, an imprint of Quarto Publishing Group USA, Inc., Minneapolis MN. 2010.

3. *Yellowstone Country. National Geographic Park Profiles.* Seymour L. Fishbein. Photographs by Raymond Gehman. Published by The National Geographic Society, The Book Division. 1997.

2.   2 Peter 3:8

ABRAHAM LINCOLN

CHAPTER 3

ABRAHAM LINCOLN AND THE ROCK ISLAND RAILROAD BRIDGE DISASTER

One of the most challenging aspects of writing about history is that the reader, looking back across time, has full knowledge of what is coming in the story. For example, try to imagine not knowing who Abraham Lincoln is or what he accomplished. Forget the image of his sixty-foot-high face on Mount Rushmore or the nineteen-foot statue of him in the Lincoln Memorial. More than one hundred fifty years after his assassination in 1865, Lincoln has become an American icon on par with George Washington in historical importance. This knowledge makes it very difficult to view him through any other lens than the one that paints him as the great man who saved the Union.

We admire his political savvy, personal decency, and persistence in the face of overwhelming disappointments. And we mourn his death at the hands of an assassin right at his moment of final victory. But in the year of 1856, virtually no one in America had any reason to suspect that Abraham Lincoln would one day be the man he became. Indeed, few people outside of select Illinois courtrooms even knew he existed. And it might have remained that way had Lincoln not been invited to join the legal team defending the Chicago and Rock Island Railroad from a liability claim. This claim, arising from an accident between a steamboat and the brand-new Rock Island Railroad Bridge spanning the Mississippi River in northern Illinois, changed the trajectory of Lincoln's life. It was both the notoriety of this case and the political contacts he made as a result of being on the defense team that were key to his meteoric rise to the presidency.

Stated another way, Abraham Lincoln may not have been elected president if the steamship *Effie Afton* had not struck the pier of the Rock Island Railroad Bridge in the late spring of 1856. One can only imagine how different our history would be had this remarkable man not been in charge during the turbulent years of the Civil War. Yet ask a thousand people if they have heard of his springboard legal case and you'll quickly find that this is a perfect example of an important forgotten story in U.S. history.

STEAMBOATS AND RAILROADS

An important element of America's economic success after the Revolutionary War was its ability to open the interior of the country to immigration and development. Technology played an essential role in this evolution. The innovation of shallow-draft steamboats that could ply the great rivers on the western side of the Appalachian Mountains was key to development. With shallow-draft boats, many inland rivers created easy paths to move people and goods, including the Ohio, Tennessee, Mississippi, and Missouri rivers. This massive river system, which drained multiple watersheds, eventually allowed steamboat traffic from New Orleans to as far north as Minnesota and Ohio.[1] Barges floated downstream, and steam-powered tugs pulled them back upstream. The elegant steamboats depicted in Currier and Ives prints carried passengers in grand style in both directions, with wood-fired boilers providing the steam needed to turn great paddle wheels against the current. By 1850, the Port of New Orleans and the city of St. Louis were the main actors on the Mississippi, and they were jealous in protecting their favored roles.

Another technological revolution began in the 1830s when railroads began operating in the United States, starting with the initiation of regular passenger service on the Baltimore & Ohio along the East Coast. While an individual steamship could carry a much greater load

---

1. A canal built between the Rock River in Illinois (a tributary of the Mississippi) and Lake Michigan actually allowed boats to travel, via the Great Lakes, from New York City, up the Hudson, across the Erie Canal, into Lake Erie, and then via the Rock River canal to the Mississippi River all the way down to New Orleans. It was a great inland water superhighway that facilitated commerce.

of cargo than a railroad train, the steamship was confined to the path of the river. Railroads were built virtually anywhere people wanted them to go. Plus, as attorney Lincoln pointed out in the Rock Island Railroad Bridge case, railroads operated in all seasons and weather. Steamboat traffic came to a standstill when the rivers iced over in the winter.

Railroad growth in the United States was astonishing, increasing from zero to nearly 30,000 miles of operating track between 1835 and 1856. When the tracks reached the eastern banks of the Mississippi River, railroad tycoons were anxious to connect even farther. The relentless growth of population in the American Midwest required rail transportation to get goods and people to and from markets.

The most logical place to do this was at Rock Island, Illinois. In 1855, the Chicago and Rock Island Railroad stretched 170 miles west from Chicago to its terminating point at Rock Island. On the opposite bank, the Missouri & Mississippi Railroad started operations at Davenport, Iowa, and reached westerly across Iowa to the Missouri River. Together, these two railroads facilitated trade and travel between the East Coast and the western frontier.

But without a bridge, all the freight had to be offloaded in Rock Island or Davenport and ferried across the river, where it was then loaded onto a different set of railroad cars. This was a huge impediment to the free flow of traffic. Of course, steamboat companies and their queen cities didn't see it that way at all—they were perfectly happy forcing everyone to use their rivers and ports.

THE ROCK ISLAND RAILROAD BRIDGE

In 1853, the Illinois legislature issued a charter for the Bridge Company, a dependent of the Chicago and Rock Island Railroad, to build a bridge across the Mississippi River.

The charter required that this new bridge "not materially obstruct or interfere with river navigation." Adding this new bridge would give Illinois a huge advantage in commerce since it already facilitated north-south traffic on the river, as well as trade via the Great Lakes. With fast rail travel from east to west, Illinois became the crossroads. Such unfettered access to world markets was truly unparalleled anywhere else in the nation.

Once approved, plans were drafted immediately. A topographical study Lieutenant Robert E. Lee (later of Civil War fame) completed in 1837 showed Rock Island to be an ideal crossing point. The bridge was to be a six-span, wooden truss structure built on seven granite piers. The largest span, which crossed the Iowa channel, was a swing bridge that could pivot parallel to the river when a steamship needed to pass through. The deepest part of the channel was the logical place for ships to pass through, and thus the swing span was planned at that location. Work on the bridge started in 1853 and was finished in 1856. The first train to cross the Mississippi River made its way from Illinois to Iowa on April 22, 1856. Railroaders cheered, while those interested in the steamboats seethed with resentment.

In fact, opposition to building the bridge began almost immediately after its announcement. Influential leaders in St. Louis objected strongly, arguing that a bridge would be a nuisance to river traffic. Supporters of the railroads felt the real reason for the riverboat owners' vehement opposition was the threat the bridge posed to their commercial interests. With an east-west rail link across the Mississippi, the majority of shipping would simply bypass St. Louis and the Missouri River, which would be an economic disaster for St. Louis.

Steamboat owners and captains also opposed the bridge because it made their lives more difficult by creating an artificial hazard to navigation at a point where the river was already tricky to manage. Just upstream from the site of the bridge were the infamous Rock Island rapids, which were so difficult to navigate that the Army Corps of Engineers had made several attempts at blasting a deeper channel. Now, with the bridge adding seven massive stone piers to the list of hazards to maneuver around, the steamship men were furious.

Even the U.S. government initially opposed the bridge. Secretary of War Jefferson Davis (future president of the Confederate States of America) was anxious over the often-discussed transcontinental railroad taking a southern route to the Pacific Ocean. He wanted the slave states to be the first to reach California. People in the South felt that California was ideal for agriculture, and no one was better suited to farming in warm latitudes than the slave-owning plantation owners. So Davis went to work to block a northern bridge, recognizing that such a structure would create political momentum for a northern railroad route to the Pacific.

With all these opposing interests lining up, it was rather remarkable that the bridge was completed. Its key to success was that Illinois and Iowa and not the federal government controlled the right of autho-rizing commerce. But even when the bridge was finished, its opponents still had an ace up their sleeve. If they could get it declared a nuisance to navigation, the federal government had jurisdiction and could order it destroyed.

That was why feelings ran so high that April morning in 1856 when the first fully loaded train chugged its way across the river.

DISASTER AT THE BRIDGE—THE *EFFIE AFTON* COLLISION AND FIRE

While the captain of a steamboat had charge of passengers and cargo, it was the riverboat pilot who had ultimate control over the boat itself. He was the one who was expert at navigating the endlessly changing nature of the river. Rivers were dynamic, creating and destroying large sandbars, submerging trees and other debris in the high water and then exposing them when the flow decreased. Sometimes entire channels disappeared as the river carved a new course. The pilot had to keep track of all of this to plot a course through the shallow rapids at various points along the river so the rocky bottom didn't tear the steamboat apart. That was why the pilot was considered king of the river.[2]

Given the responsibility and skill of these pilots, it is puzzling that on May 6, 1856, the pilot of the steamboat *Effie Afton* chose to race past another steamboat while going upstream. He made this maneuver just before reaching the central pier of the brand-new Rock Island Rail-road Bridge. Making this vanity pass forced him closer to the pier than a normal approach would have provided, but even so, the *Effie Afton* successfully made it through the main channel with good power and no contact with the bridge. Additionally, the turntable that supported the swinging segment of the deck was duly opened so the smokestacks of the steamboat passed through unimpeded.

What happened next initiated the legal action against the Bridge Company. Just as the *Effie Afton* cleared the north end of the long pier on which the turntable was balanced, the right-side paddle wheel slowed relative to the left paddle wheel. This caused the boat to veer sharply into the current while losing forward momentum. The force of the current quickly pulled the boat back downstream and into a collision with the

---

2.   See Mark Twain's *Life on the Mississippi* for a marvelous discussion of the training and expertise of riverboat pilots.

THE ROCK ISLAND RAILROAD BRIDGE

pier, where it lodged against the stonework. The force of the crash was so great that ashes from toppled stoves in the passenger staterooms started numerous fires.

Many observed this calamity both from the shore and on other boats on the river. Onlookers immediately began running to the bridge to render assistance while the passengers on board the *Effie Afton* panicked at the thought of being caught in the river on a burning boat.

Fortunately, the initial fires were extinguished quickly, and an escape plan was implemented for passengers to climb up the massive rock pier to the safety of the bridge above. All the passengers were safely evacuated, although livestock remained on board.

This is where the story really gets interesting. Even though the steamboat was wedged firmly against the pier and the fires had been put out, a new fire broke out shortly after the last passenger was evacuated. This fire burned with greater intensity than the first fires—quickly spreading to the superstructure of the wooden railroad bridge. The north end of the swing span went up in flames, and according to a newspaper account in the *Chicago Democratic Press*, it collapsed onto the wreckage of the steamboat. With one side of the swing span gone, the other was out of balance, so it was cut loose to fall into the river. At that point, the *Effie Afton* broke free of the pier, allowing the wreckage of both the bridge superstructure and the steamboat to drift down the river in flames. The animals on board the burning ship did not survive.

In less than an hour, the main span of the bridge was destroyed, the steamboat was a complete loss, and all the cargo was gone. *Effie Afton* came to an end. But the litigation that was to follow soon occupied the national stage and provided unexpected visibility to Abraham Lincoln, a member of the defense team.

Rejoicing on the River
One would think a disaster like this would elicit instant sympathy from the other steamboat crews on the river. Instead, the other crews sounded their boat whistles and rang their bells in jubilation at the destruction of the bridge. This showed the depth of hostility the riverboat captains and pilots felt toward the hated railroad bridge.

Claims and Counterclaims
There was no question that the steamboat owners would file a lawsuit for damages against the Bridge Company/Chicago and Rock Island Railroad and the Mississippi and Missouri Railroad (owner of the Davenport side of the bridge). After all, it was the collision with the bridge that destroyed the *Effie Afton*. But their lawsuit aimed far higher than mere remuneration for a lost boat; the plaintiffs wanted a decision of the court declaring the bridge to be a nuisance and hazard to interstate traffic. If the plaintiffs prevailed, the entire bridge would have to be destroyed and the seven stone piers removed from the riverbed. Considering the enormous sum of money spent to build the bridge, to say nothing of the interruption to east-west railroad traffic, these were enormous stakes indeed.

However, those with railroad interests were suspicious. The unusual power failure on just one side of the steamboat after successfully clearing the pier on the upstream passage seemed unnatural. The railroaders concluded that the *Effie Afton*'s owner, in league with other St. Louis interests, had instructed the captain to intentionally wreck the boat.

A second cause of suspicion was that the *Effie Afton* was insured for $15,000 coverage but for fire damage only. There was no insurance for damage from river hazards, even though such coverage was available. This raised the question of whether the captain had ordered the setting of the second fire. One way or another, the owner of the boat wanted either the insurance company or the bridge owners to pay for the loss of the *Effie Afton*.

With so much at stake, it's little wonder that the best lawyers in the Midwest were engaged to represent both parties in the lawsuit.

ABRAHAM LINCOLN AND THE TRIAL

Captain John Hurd, the owner of the *Effie Afton*, filed suit in the U.S. District Court at Chicago, demanding reparations from the Bridge Company for loss of ship and cargo. The complaint held that the boat was carefully navigated but that the powerful crosscurrents and eddies the bridge piers caused drove the ship into the bridge.

The defense, which attorney Norman B. Judd led, contended that the *Effie Afton's* destruction was the result of equipment failure and lack of care on the part of the acting pilot. In his opening statement, Judd also alleged that riverboat interests premeditated the collision to intentionally burn the bridge. This, of course, elicited an outraged response from the plaintiffs that no such conspiracy existed.

The plaintiffs alleged that the question before the court was simple: was the bridge a material impediment to the free navigation of the river? If so, payment for damages was due, and the bridge had to be destroyed. The trial began on September 8, 1857.

Lincoln's role in all this? He was given the most important task—closing arguments for the defense team. By this

ABRAHAM LINCOLN

point in his life, Lincoln was a prosperous, successful railroad lawyer, having won three cases for the Alton & Sangamon Railroad that eventually came before the U.S. Supreme Court. He had also argued two cases involving the question of the obstruction of navigable rivers by bridges—one time representing the railroad, the other time the riverboats. Thus, he was well informed on both sides of the issue and was known for his thorough preparation and forceful presentation style.

The plaintiffs went first, calling the *Effie Afton* captain and pilot to testify. Their witness list also included numerous other riverboat captains who had an opinion on the difficulty of getting past the new bridge. In all, dozens of witnesses talked about what a nightmare it was to try to get through the river channel.

But the credibility of their testimonies was called into question on cross-examination. For example, Nathaniel Parker, a pilot on board as a passenger that day, admitted under cross that he witnessed two other boats make it successfully through the draw prior to the *Effie Afton*'s collision. He also admitted that he had passed safely by the bridge two times in other boats prior to this incident and at least a dozen times after. Half a dozen other plaintiff witnesses were also forced to admit they had made multiple passages without any problems.

The next line of attack on the bridge was that the pier placement, at an angle to the riverbed, caused cross currents. The steamboat owners asserted this caused eddies that turned the *Effie Afton*, swinging her to the right immediately after her making it past the bridge. Their theory was that dividing the natural channel into two channels around the pier affected the natural flow of water, which caused the accident.

Finally, the owners indicated that the fires that destroyed both the boat and some spans of the bridge were the inevitable consequence of the hazard the bridge created. The human and animal suffering incurred showed the malicious result of the bridge's construction.

The sum of their argument was that navigation on the river should be the same after the building of a bridge as it was before; otherwise, a nuisance and hazard had in fact been created. In the case of the Rock Island Railroad Bridge, navigation clearly was not the same, and, therefore, the owner of the steamboat was entitled to compensation, and the bridge should come down.

The defendants (the Bridge Company) countered these claims with thirty witnesses of their own. In preparation for questioning these witnesses,

Abraham Lincoln took time before the trial to travel from Chicago to Rock Island, where he walked out on the bridge to assess the situation. Toward the center, above the point where the collision occurred, he encountered a boy sitting on the span. When Lincoln asked if he lived nearby, the boy said he lived in Davenport and that his father was the engineer who had built the bridge. Impressed, Lincoln asked the boy to help him figure out how fast the water ran through the channels on each side of the bridge. To do this, they carefully timed how fast a log traveled from the island to the bridge. Lincoln spent the better part of the day familiarizing himself with all aspects of the bridge and the river.

To add to this first-hand knowledge of the site, Lincoln also engaged a team of engineers to complete "float trials." These trials tested the direction of the current. A float, attached to submerged rods of varying lengths, was put in upstream of the bridge and was allowed to float under the bridge. If there were any eddies or cross-currents, the floats would discover them. These professional engineering trials confirmed that the original engineering studies in which 500 to 800 floats had been used to calculate the best angle of placement for the pier were accurate. They also proved to Lincoln's satisfaction that the bridge piers created no eddies whatsoever. In fact, the off-angle placement of the pier actually smoothed the free flow of water under the bridge. This knowledge would play a significant role in his summation of the trial.

But before that happened, the defense put forward some key arguments for the jury to consider.

First, they used their own witnesses and the conflicting cross-examination of plaintiff witnesses to show that many hundreds of successful passages had been made under the bridge with no accidents. This, they asserted, proved that it was not an unreasonable impediment to river traffic.

Second, they called on the bridge design engineer, Benjamin Brayton, to explain in detail to the jury how each of the seven piers came to be sited. He said that the main pier in question was positioned so that during low water, only 10.5 percent of the 1,322 feet of the passage was obstructed. Because the piers tapered as they gained height, only 8.5 percent was blocked in high water. He also testified that the rapids upstream constituted a much greater challenge to navigation than did the bridge.

Third, the defense used the float studies, as well as other water-flow analysis, to show that the current was entirely predictable for a certified pilot who took the time to study the passage. The successful passage of hundreds of ships had proven it was possible. They argued that in this particular case, the pilot had just not exercised care and preparation.

Fourth, some witnesses testified that Captain Hurd of the *Effie Afton* said at the time of the accident that the problem was the failure of mechanical equipment on the starboard side of the steamboat (right side). This failure caused the right paddle wheel to lose speed in relation to the left paddle wheel. The inevitable turning action that comes from one paddle wheel turning while the other is idle caused the boat to swing perpendicular to the current. This power failure, they asserted, was the real cause of the collision—not a cross-current, not the bridge, but mechanical failure on the steamboat for which the Bridge Company had no responsibility.

Finally, they brought forward witnesses who suggested that the second fire had been intentionally started because the captain had acknowledged that the insurance would pay for only fire damage, not collisions. While there was no proof that this was what happened, the fact that the captain had alluded to it immediately after the original fires had been extinguished gave room for reasonable doubt.

After several weeks of trial, it fell to Lincoln to summarize all this in a way that would convince the jury that the defendant Bridge Company was innocent. This was where Lincoln's skill as a litigator came out. He began by telling the jury that he had no intention of attacking anyone on either side of the trial but that he would probably become earnest as he developed his line of reasoning. But he hoped he would not become ill-natured.[3] He then proceeded to use some sharp rhetorical weapons against the plaintiffs. In spite of his assurance of goodwill, he used innuendo to accuse the St. Louis riverboat interests. He mocked the hypocrisy of the plaintiff's witnesses who blew their steamboat whistles in jubilation when the bridge caught fire but who, when in the courtroom, assumed an attitude of disinterest. He referred to his own float studies to demonstrate that the bridge had been built as skillfully as possible to mitigate any interruption to the natural flow of the river. And he used sarcasm to discredit the lead plaintiff's attorney's objections that "floats are not boats," arguing that "Mr. Wead did not indulge us with an argument in support of this statement. Is it because there is a difference in size? Will not a small body and

---

3.   *Lincoln's Greatest Case: The River, the Bridge, and the Making of America.* McGinty, Brian (2015-02-09). Liveright. Kindle Edition 149–152.

a large one float the same way under the same influence? True, a flatboat will float faster than an eggshell and the eggshell might be blown away by the wind, but if under the same influence, they would go the same way. Logs, floats, boards, various things the witnesses say all show the same current."[4]

Finally, Lincoln asserted that the plaintiffs belief that river navigation should be the same with or without a bridge was simply unrealistic. To accept such a position would lead to a public policy of banning all bridges across all rivers in the United States. He cited the fact that more than 12,000 freight cars and nearly 75,000 passengers had crossed the reconstructed Rock Island Railroad Bridge in the year since the *Effie Afton* collision. This clearly showed that railroad commerce was every bit as essential to the future growth of the country as was riverboat traffic.

Lincoln next argued that since both the Illinois and Iowa legislatures had authorized the bridge, it was clear that the citizens of those states had an interest in the success of both the railroads and the steamboats. To assert, as did the plaintiffs, that the riverboats needed to make no accommodation whatsoever was both unrealistic and contrary to the live-and-let-live attitude that was making the United States so successful economically.

Lincoln also addressed two other arguments the plaintiffs had put forward: that a suspension bridge or tunnel should have been built instead of the multiple truss, swinging bridge design that had been selected. Lincoln demonstrated that the cost of a suspension bridge, both in construction and operation, was unreasonable. He added sarcastically that if a taller bridge had been built, the steamboats would have made their funnels ever more towering so they could continue to fight the bridge's right to exist. To the last argument, he said quietly that tunnels under the river were simply not an option given the technology of the times.

Lincoln concluded the case for the defense after two days of arguments. The jury voted nine to three in favor of the Bridge Company, meaning a hung verdict. Even so, both sides viewed it as a victory for the bridge since a hung jury meant that no damages were authorized and the bridge was safe from the threat of being dismantled. It was a great victory for Lincoln and the other lawyers on his team.

---

4.   Ibid.

It's interesting that several years later a similar case was brought to the Supreme Court, which essentially sided with all of Lincoln's arguments in favor of the right of railroads to coexist with steamboat interests.

POLITICAL RAMIFICATIONS

Prior to this case, Lincoln had been known only slightly outside of Illinois. He had served one relatively undistinguished term in the U.S. House of Representatives but had returned to his law practice after just two years. But after the Rock Island Railroad Bridge case, Norman Judd, the lead attorney on behalf of the Bridge Company, viewed Lincoln as a skillful pragmatist. He believed Lincoln was uniquely qualified to argue the cause of preserving the Union to a national audience. The intense nationwide interest in the bridge lawsuit had propelled Lincoln's name and legal expertise well beyond the state of Illinois. So Judd became an influential political supporter of Lincoln. In fact, his endorsement was critical to Lincoln's success in moving forward as a leader of the new Republican party. Just three years later, Abraham Lincoln was elected as president of the United States. From that point forward, his personal and political history is well known.

SUMMARY

Lincoln's quick rise from obscurity to the pinnacle of power was astonishing. Even more remarkable was the fact that there was a very real chance it would never have happened except for this interesting case and the important role he played in its outcome.

A railroad helped Lincoln become president. And as president, he would clear the way for the world's greatest railroad—the transcontinental railroad—that would meld east and west, just as the Civil War melded north and south.

SOURCES

1. *Lincoln's Greatest Case: The River, the Bridge, and the Making of America.* Brian McGinty. 2015. Liveright. Kindle Edition.

2. "Bridging the Mississippi: The Railroads and Steamboats Clash at the Rock Island Railroad Bridge." David A. Pfeiffer. Prologue. NARA (National Archives) Summer 2004, Volume 36, No. 2.

Nearing full colapse of the Teton Dam

CHAPTER 4

COLLAPSE OF THE TETON DAM

AN OMINOUS PREDICTION

While attending college, I experienced one of those moments that didn't make a big impression at the time but, when looking back, had great significance. It was 1972, and I was a freshman at Idaho State University in Pocatello, sitting in my most difficult class of the semester: geology. It's not that the class was uninteresting; it's that I was mostly incapable of telling the difference between an igneous and metamorphic rock, which is a big problem for any would-be geologist. On this particular day, the graduate student teaching our class told us he was ending class early so he could go to Idaho Falls. He and other geologists intended to protest the Bureau of Reclamation's proposed Teton Dam near Newdale, Idaho, some 80 miles north of Pocatello.

When asked why he opposed the dam, he replied that the dam site was geologically unstable, and the foundation would rest on an extremely permeable rock base. "This is," he said dramatically, "a disaster in the making." Having piqued our curiosity, he used this as an opportunity to bring geology into the real world. "Rhyolite and basalt are volcanic rocks that are very porous," he explained. "Water seepage into large fissures in the rock base makes it a crazy place to build a dam."

He further explained that while the Bureau planned to inject concrete grout into these fissures, it was the opinion of area geologists that it would still be unstable. The sheer weight of the vast reservoir would inevitably compromise the grout curtain. Thus, the dam's foundation could fail.

Finally, he discussed the fact that there had been five earthquakes near the dam site in just the previous decade, which also made it a poor choice for a dam. We all knew that our part of the world rested on a geographically hot area. Yellowstone Park, with all its earthquake activity, was less than 100 miles from the dam site. The Craters of the Moon National Monument, which protected eerie-looking lava flows that were active as recently as when Columbus discovered America, was only 80 miles to the southwest. "In sum," he concluded, "this is a terrible project that needs to be stopped!"

I was fascinated both by dams and disasters, so this raised my curiosity. But as I thought about it on my way home from class, I concluded that our graduate student was probably just a crank. After all, the Bureau of Reclamation wouldn't build a dam on a site that wasn't safe—that just didn't make sense. If you can't trust the government, who can you trust? So I forgot about it.

That is, until four years later when, on Saturday, June 5, 1976, nearly everyone in Eastern Idaho anxiously watched on television as a gaping crater formed on the front of the newly completed Teton Dam. It was an enormous earthen dam: 305 feet high and as wide as the length of ten football fields. In just a few months, it had already impounded a vast reservoir that had filled much faster than planned because of heavy snowmelt in the nearby Grand Teton watershed.

News of a problem at the dam had first reached a local television station, KID of Idaho Falls, after a family of tourists saw a dark spot appear on the northwestern face of the dam. Employees of the Bureau had first detected a new leak near the toe of the dam at 7:45 a.m. and had called construction personnel back to the site to work on the problem. Then the wet spot appeared farther up. They deployed two Caterpillar tractors to move large rocks to cover the spot on the face of the dam. Other operators at the crest of the dam worked to force more rocks down into the reservoir on the upstream side, where the water leakage originated.

When water started flowing openly from the trouble spot, the Caterpillar operators worked with increasing intensity, trying to staunch the flow, but the water was getting ahead of them. By this time, a reporter and a photographer from KID had arrived by airplane and had gone to a live "Breaking News" feed from directly above the dam.

In one of the most heart-stopping moments of my life, I watched as the Caterpillar operators suddenly jumped from their heavy machines and ran as fast as they could up the face of the dam. The hole was growing so fast that it required ropes to pull them to safety. Once safe and standing on the side of the canyon wall above the breach, they watched helplessly as the turgid brown water swallowed their Caterpillars, the machines disappearing right into the interior of the dam.

Of course, this signaled that the unthinkable was about to happen, and within a matter of minutes, water arced out from the wound on the dam's surface. A whirlpool appeared in the reservoir above the dam, sucking water with increasing ferocity from the lake right into the dam itself. Unbelievably, in less than four hours from when the first spot appeared at 7:45 a.m., the top of the dam collapsed into an immense wall of water and mud. This water raced down the narrow canyon toward the communities of Newdale and Sugar City, as well as the Snake River cities of Rexburg, Idaho Falls, and Blackfoot.

Workers at the scene described their feeling as surreal, given that they had spent the previous four years building this massive dam and were now watching it melt into mud in a matter of minutes. It was a sight no one in modern America had ever witnessed, since the Bureau of Reclamation had not yet built a dam that had failed.

It was only at this point, as I looked in disbelief at the television images, that the memory of my unique experience in a geology class four years earlier came to mind. Our graduate student was clearly not a crank, and this unfolding disaster had occurred in spite of warnings issued before a single shovelful of dirt had been moved. A tragedy was now unfolding that would affect the lives of more than 100,000 people in Southeastern Idaho, people whose homes and businesses now lay directly in the path of the oncoming water. Eleven people would die, along with more than 13,000 head of cattle and countless other animals. Damage was estimated to have exceeded $2 billion. It was a modern epic that few Americans remember today.

BUILDING AND FILLING THE DAM

There was a lot of political pressure by local farmers and business owners to build the dam. They wanted the many benefits that come from having a wild river like the Teton controlled by a reservoir. These advantages included flood control, power generation, and a steady flow of water through the dry summer months. In 1961, the area had suffered a severe drought, followed by flooding in 1962. A dam in the area could have mitigated both these conditions.

With intense pressure from Idaho's elected officials, Congress authorized the new Teton Dam in 1963. It took until 1971 to complete all the necessary studies, including an environmental impact study that mentioned some of the known failings of the site. But none of these studies suggested the possibility of a collapse. Contracts were let out in 1971, and construction started late in 1972.

As actual excavation began, new problems emerged at the dam site that went well beyond the permeability problem. In fact, they found large fissures in the canyon walls, some as large as caves, in which people could walk upright. Test grouting absorbed everything the contractors could pump into the ground, and ultimately the contractor used twice as much grout than called for in the specifications. But even at that, no one could tell if it was enough since the foundation just absorbed everything they could pump into it.

In spite of this, no one was able to halt the project. A later investigation by the U.S. House of Representatives concluded that finding the caves should have cast doubt on the Bureau's ability to fill all the empty voids. But even after the dam failed, the Bureau stood by their assertion that the grouting should have been sufficient. They attributed failure to another unknowable cause. That leaves things a little unsettled. A dam inspector I spoke with believes the primary cause of failure was completing so much of the work in the midst of a very cold winter. The cold adversely affects both the curing of concrete in the footings and the compaction of fill materials in the dam.

What is certain is the dam filled much faster than planned because of a heavy spring runoff, which was more than a thousand times greater than initially anticipated. The reservoir filled at the rate of four feet per day. The usual practice is to fill earthen dams slowly over several seasons so that the inevitable settling of the reservoir floor will cause the least movement of the earth as possible. But that didn't happen at the Teton Dam. The pool reached full capacity of 240 feet in just a single season, even though the primary outlets and emergency spillway gates were incomplete. Thus, the only way to let water out of the dam was through the emergency outlet works, which couldn't have begun to release as much water as was flowing into the reservoir.

That was when nature went to work to create its own outlet.

COLLAPSE OF THE DAM

The appearance of muddy water seeping from the base of the dam did alert engineers that something was going on, but it was simply beyond imagination to think it was serious. Seepage was normal as new dams filled. But anxiety rose when the wet spot appeared near the top of the dam since that was not normal. That was when the bulldozers were called in to seal the leak. But by then, it was too late. Simply adding more material to the front of the dam did nothing to seal the interior damage. Water on the face of the barrier meant that the supposedly impermeable core of Zone 1 at the center of the dam was compromised.

THE TETON DAM BEGINS TO RUPTURE

THE TETON DAM COLLAPSE ACCELERATES

Perhaps a quick discussion of earthen dams will help. Dams are constructed in vertical slices, with the slice in the center made of extremely fine material that, when compressed, becomes impermeable to water. Usually this narrow band that extends from the base of the dam to the crest is clay or concrete, and slightly more coarse material is added to both sides of the impermeable layer and fans out at the base. Then a wider and even rougher layer is laid down until the outer reach of the pyramid shape is bolstered by hefty boulders that give the dam the weight it needs to resist the pressure of the reservoir. The primary requirement for an earthen dam is that its total weight has to exceed the weight of the lake. Thus, it's called a gravity dam. The incredible weight of the water in the reservoir presses against the wall of the pyramid and compresses all the layers against each other, further solidifying its impermeable nature. There is always some natural leakage from under the base of the dam, which poses no threat to the structure, but natural seepage should always be clear. Muddy seepage indicates erosion. Either the foundation is turning to mud, or the dam itself is losing material.

In the case of the Teton Dam, the appearance of the wet spot was a sure indicator that the dam had been compromised. At 11:15 a.m., officials at the dam site instructed the county sheriff's office to evacuate people from the downstream communities as a precaution. It was just a few minutes later when the two Caterpillar operators were pulled to safety.

At 11:55 a.m., the crest of the dam collapsed into the reservoir. Two minutes later, one-third of the dam wall disintegrated into a partition of muddy water. The six-mile canyon below the dam became a raging torrent as the lake emptied. Once out of the canyon, the water spread out on the broad, flat plain, but its path was inevitable; it was on its way to the Snake River, a major river in Idaho that ultimately emptied into the Columbia River on its way to the Pacific Ocean. As the flood sloshed out onto this plain, more than a dozen communities and hundreds of farms lay in its path. Its only checkpoint lay sixty miles to the south, the American Falls Reservoir.

FEAR FOR AMERICAN FALLS DAM

One can only imagine the feelings of the water master of the American Falls Dam when he received a call indicating that the Teton Dam had collapsed. He knew all of that water was on its way to his reservoir.

The American Falls Dam, completed in 1927, was, at the time, a concrete dam built across a relatively broad depression in the Snake River plain near the small community of American Falls, Idaho, just north of the beautiful basalt falls of the Snake River. The American Falls Reservoir was much larger than the Teton Dam Reservoir but had also experienced heavy runoff that year. Most worrisome was the fact that this dam's concrete had already been compromised. In a 1960s sample from the dam's core, authorities discovered that an adverse chemical reaction was occurring inside the concrete, degrading it so much that the Bureau of Reclamation sought authority to replace the dam with a much heavier modern dam. Work was scheduled to begin on this rebuilding project in 1978—still two years in the future.

With the flood of the Teton Reservoir headed their way, the engineers at American Falls began to release as much water as the outlet works could handle. But with less than a week until Teton's reservoir water

THE TETON DAM COMPLETELY FAILS 11:55 A.M., JUNE 5, 1976

would arrive, this maximum release would have little impact. Those living in the area followed the progress of the water as it worked its way down the Snake River, wondering what would happen if the American Falls Dam were overtopped.

I remember talking to friends who said that if the American Falls Dam failed, it could start a domino effect on all the dams on the Snake River all the way into the Columbia. The unfolding tragedy was fertile soil for vivid imaginations!

As it turns out, our fears were unfounded. The reservoir completely absorbed the additional water, rising to just below the emergency spillways but not actually triggering an excess release. All the dams below American Falls were safe. Two years later, the American Falls Reservoir was slowly emptied so work could begin on a massive new dam that is far more muscular than the one it replaced. This time the Bureau took no chances and built a structure more than equal to its design conditions.

CITIES IN CRISIS

Wilford and Sugar City, Idaho, were the first communities hit by the flood. They were virtually wiped out, with more than 80 percent of their buildings destroyed by the wall of water that washed over them. When the wave hit Rexburg, which was more densely populated, it encountered a lumberyard and immediately dispersed these massive logs, turning them into projectiles that slammed into nearby bulk gasoline storage tanks. The tanks exploded, igniting the logs and adding to the destruction downstream as the flood smashed into buildings in the central section of the city of Rexburg. The combination of fire and water destroyed the historical and commercial center of the town.

It should be noted that not all of the city was destroyed. The south side of Rexburg, including Brigham Young University–Idaho (then called Ricks College) and many residences, was elevated on hills that overlook the commercial district. The water sloshed up onto these hills but quickly turned to follow the natural contour of the land and leave that part of the city unharmed.

Once past Rexburg, the water flowed west to the small towns of Roberts and Menan. They absorbed the brunt of all the debris before the water hit

HE SURVIVED GRUELING DUEL WITH WATER, LOGS

Blackfoot Morning News Special Edition, June 11, 1976

"I didn't know what was going on. I saw a big wave and told him to jump. I never saw him after that."

That's how 22-year old Daryl Griggs of St. Anthony, Idaho remembered the start of what was to be a long, long afternoon June 5, 1976.

Griggs and his buddy of 10 years, 21-year-old David Benson of Teton, were fishing on an island about three miles downstream from Teton Dam, just below Newdale.

They had waded across the stream to the island. The water had been waist high.

They had been there about an hour, just using worms and spinners. They went fishing often, and did a lot of things together.

"It was just a normal day," Griggs recalled. Then the water rose five or six feet and we were waist high in water.

"I didn't know what was going on.

I saw a big wave and told David to jump. I never saw him after that.

"All of a sudden I was just surrounded by a big log jam. I got caught in a whole bunch of log jams. There were 20 and 30-foot waves. They (logs) would go down in the water and just shoot back up.

"I was hanging on logs. They tightened up and I got crushed. All the way down, for about three miles, I was hanging on for my life.

"I just knew the whole time I was dead. I knew I was a goner. I knew I was going to drown.

"I didn't know what to do. I was thrown about a lot. Right near the end I was still hanging on and my legs were dragging on the ground.

"I never gave up. I knew I had been crushed. I just wondered what was going on. I wondered where he (Benson) was.

"Then I was pinned to a tree. I just kind of squirmed my way up it. That took me 45 minutes.

"Nobody could see me in the tree. I was up there a couple of hours. Then I started yelling and some people heard me."

a juncture and finally joined the Henry's Fork of the Snake River. Now the flood traveled due south through the largest city in the area—Idaho Falls. Blackfoot was the last community impacted by the flood. Below that, the water passed through fields until it reached the American Falls Reservoir.

Griggs knew he was hurt. He thought he had a punctured lung and later at the Idaho Falls Hospital that condition was confirmed.

Griggs had to have help to get down [from the tree]. By this time air was under his skin. His eyes were tightly closed and it would be another 24 hours before he could see.

"I don't think I could have lasted much longer. I was pretty weak. I didn't really give up all the way down but in my mind I didn't have a chance."

Griggs spent the next 10 days in the hospital. Then he was released, on the way to recovery from serious lung damage and five broken ribs.

It will be another two months before the 6-2 Griggs could return to his job at a lumber company. He normally weighs 160 to 165 pounds but when released from the hospital weighed only 135 pounds.

What did Griggs think about the dam breaking?

"I just don't know," he responded. "I have different opinions about things. They said it had been leaking since that morning. At least I figure they should have warned people. It would have saved some lives...."

"I was in a daze for quite a while. I can remember seeing a house wiped out as I was in the water. I saw a barn get it. I saw lots of debris and logs. I remember looking north toward Wilford and all I could see was water."

Used by permission. Joe Williams, editor of the Blackfoot Morning News. February 2016.

—*Lamar Crosby, Blackfoot News Staff Writer.* Source: *Tragedy: A chronology of the Teton Dam disaster.* Bulletin Publishing Co., Inc. 27 N.W. Main, Blackfoot, Idaho 83221. June 11, 1976.

Because it took almost twenty-four hours for the water to reach Idaho Falls, city leaders had some time to prepare. They called for thousands of volunteers to sandbag along the river. It should be noted that the slope of the land in Idaho Falls was favorable to funneling the flow of the water through a relatively narrow zone in the business district. Commercial buildings were destroyed, but most residential areas in Idaho Falls were unharmed. Blackfoot had a similar experience.

The federal government, under the direction of President Gerald Ford, paid out more than 7,500 claims, totaling more than 300 million dollars. Today, the remnants of the Teton Dam still remain in a now-isolated spot between Rexburg and Driggs, Idaho, on the western slopes of the Grand Teton Mountains. More than two-thirds of the dam is still in place, and the overflow spillway now towers hundreds of feet above the small river at the base of the dam. The Teton River quietly wends its way through the narrow gap that washed out in 1976. The scouring effect of the water being forced through the narrow canyon at such terrific velocity destroyed much of the natural ecology of the Teton River, and downstream, much of the topsoil in the once-fertile plains below the dam was washed away, leaving the ground mostly barren.

Since the failure of the Teton Dam, and in order to make sure similar mistakes are not made, the Bureau of Reclamation has instituted new protocols when new dams are proposed. They've also established new procedures to monitor existing structures and to check for structural integrity and stress so repairs can be made or the dams retired or replaced.

Interestingly, a follow-up study the University of Washington conducted suggests an alternate theory for the failure of the Teton Dam. Rather than poor foundation conditions, this study posits that the primary cause of failure was from cracks in the impermeable layer due to improper fill material. Once the reservoir reached these cracks, it did what water does naturally, which is start to flow. The official conclusion credits both conditions—seepage under the grout cap (which most people believe) or the alternate theory of cracking caused by hydraulic fracturing of the core material. Both conditions were aggravated by the rapid filling of the reservoir beyond design parameters.

Forty years later, and even after all the damage and loss of life, there are people who still believe the dam should be rebuilt.

A WORKER'S INSIGHT

Jim Roker worked for Morrison-Knudsen as a highly skilled heavy-transport driver. He carried oversized, heavy equipment, such as Caterpillar tractors and giant cranes, to and from and around the worksite. He was at the dam site on the very first day work began, with an assignment to help clear snow so the first employees could reach their assigned areas, and he continued through postfailure cleanup. Today, almost forty years later, he still fishes on the Teton River near the remnants of the dam.

He and I talked for more than an hour in the summer of 2015. What surprised me from Jim's interview, and from the company's *Em-Kayan* magazines he'd saved all these years, was just how massive this project was. Jim stressed that Morrison-Knudsen built the Teton Dam to far stricter construction standards than any project before it. For example, he spoke of traveling to the St. Anthony Sand Dunes thirty miles northwest of the site to bring in the highest quality sand to mix in the concrete aggregate. He also moved rock-crushing equipment to Fall River because the rock there had extremely high break strength. The resulting concrete was the highest quality ever used on a dam, measured by its break strength. This concrete was used in lining the diversion tunnels and constructing the outlet plant, spillways, and a power plant. It was also utilized in the grout curtain injected beneath the dam's footings. The ten million yards of material employed in the dam's construction was laid down layer by layer in five zones, using the materials specified in the construction contract with the federal government. These materials were composed of "impervious silt, sand and gravel, sand, gravel and cobbles, miscellaneous material, and 'shot rock,' which was used to protect the slopes of the dam and finished with quarried riprap on the upstream face."[1]

A 1974 issue of the *Em-Kayan* proudly proclaims that the dam had reached 50 percent completion, and the December 1975 issue celebrates the fact that the "Teton Dam 'Tops Out' on Schedule." Reading these magazines from before the failure, when almost no one could imagine what was coming, is almost eerie because of the writers' lack of awareness. For example, the writers proudly discuss the extraordinary measures taken to build the dam:

- Two 700-foot keyways on each side.

1.   *The Em-Kayan*, Vol. 33, December, 1974, No. 10, 6–8. Published by Morrison-Knudsen Company, Inc. Syms-York Co., Boise, Idaho.

- A 100-foot-deep trench below the base of the dam filled with grout more than 300 feet deep.

- The base was sealed with impervious silt to form the base of the dam.

- Impervious silt formed the core.

Looking back from the perspective of the twenty-first century, we know that dam was not impervious at all, but these publications projected nothing but optimism and pride. That the entire structure could fail in less than an hour seemed impossible then and is incredible even now.

Jim was not at the dam site when it failed, but he had been there the night before, removing some trash gates so workers could cut a ditch for the leakage coming out at the base of the dam. Here is Jim's story in his own words:

On Friday night, it was evident that some water had got between the fill and the base and had started washing near the base of the dam. This was not unusual in earth-filled dams, so no one was concerned. But they did want to cut a ditch to control the flow of this water, so they had me come to the base of the dam. When I'd arrived at the site earlier in the day, I had moved some equipment down through the spillways ahead of the gates. When I came back a few hours later I couldn't get back to the same spot because there was a lot of water in the spillway—it was that full.

We all attributed this to the fact that the dam had filled so quickly because of heavy spring runoff. But rather than see this as something dangerous, most people were satisfied that this proved the worth of the dam. Rather than causing flooding, this excess runoff had been fully contained, which was a primary purpose of the dam.

Even with that, I do remember something that, in retrospect, was quite ominous. In the weeks leading up to the disaster, I had hauled a large crane to the edge of the reservoir, where it was transferred to a barge. Divers had been brought in from Twin Falls, Idaho, to guide a hook down to a plug in the concrete intake structure that needed to be opened by the crane. The scuba divers had been told that the water would be approximately 25 feet deep, but because of the heavy flow into the reservoir, it was actually almost 100 feet deep. When they got into the water, they found that it was extremely murky from turbulence. The conditions were so severe that the younger scuba diver refused to go in, but the more experienced diver said he would give it a try. He was successful, but there was so much pressure at that depth that an air release hose that wasn't properly secured to the intake structure broke free and started flagellating in the water. The hose whipped the poor scuba diver as he made his way to the surface. When we got him to safety, he told us that the water was so murky that he couldn't see his own hand in front of his face. It didn't make sense that water at such great depth and so near the dam would have that volume of suspended material in it. But the thing that startled me the most is that when I returned to that spot just one week later the water level had risen to nearly 200 feet. In just one week, I didn't have to back my trailer nearly so far down into the reservoir to retrieve the crane. Just imagine a lake that size filling almost 100 feet in a single week! When the call came to me on June 5 that the dam was failing, I immediately told my wife to call everyone we knew because I was fully aware of just how much water was in that canyon!

While I don't think that anyone expected the dam to fail, the rapid filling did cause concern. We couldn't open the main gates because the companion flanges weren't installed, and they were critical to the doors' operation. I remember some of the experienced people were very anxious to get these gates open to reduce the pressure on the rapidly filling reservoir. In fact, on the morning of the dam collapse, my wife had taken a call asking if I knew where the companion flanges were. If they had been successful in opening the main tunnels, they could have released a great deal of water very quickly because they were colossal tubes. But, of course, their efforts were too late, and by the time I got home, word was out that the dam had already failed. I couldn't have helped, anyway, since I didn't know where the flanges were.

When the dam broke, the water rushed down into the canyon, where it encountered large cottonwood trees. These giant trees, with their extensive branches and leaves, actually impeded the flow of the water temporarily, as did the large logs that were used in the construction of the dam. In fact, the sheer volume of debris that was torn up by the onrushing water actually formed temporary barriers up Hog Hollow near Wilford, Idaho, which caused a second surge when they broke. But anything that slowed the water was a godsend to the people below. There were no cellphones in 1976, so people below the dam had to get the word out by using landline telephones, and by sheriff and police cars driving out to warn people to get out.

The people closest to the dam were in the greatest danger. After the flood, I talked with some of the survivors. One lady's experience tells the story: When she went out of her house to see what was going on, she looked upstream and saw the large irrigation sprinkler pipes being tossed up into the air like giant Pixie sticks. That's when she knew she was in imminent danger. She immediately ran to an old car that didn't often start, but on this occasion she said a prayer and the car started on her first try. She drove at high speed for high ground. When she returned the next day there was nothing left of her house or farm; everything had been destroyed and washed away, including the concrete foundation of her house. It looked very much like images of a moonscape, with no vegetation and even the topsoil scoured away.

Another person I met lived in Wilford near the top of the canyon. He was changing his irrigation water when he felt the ground start to tremble under his feet. This fellow said that he looked upstream and saw a massive cloud of dust and what looked like a giant herd of Hereford cattle running up the sides of the canyons. Of course that couldn't be the case, so he peered more intently. His heart raced when he figured out that a wall of water was jamming fir trees up against the side of the canyon walls, in the process shredding their red bark from the trunks and sending it up as a cloud of dust.

When he realized what was going on, he kicked off his thick rubber irrigation boots and ran to the nearest part of the road where he was picked up by a neighbor. They started driving frantically toward the neighbor's house to make sure his daughter wasn't there, and when they found that the house was empty, they started racing towards St. Anthony to the north. He said the intersections were very dangerous because people were going 80 miles per hour trying to escape the oncoming water. My farmer friend arrived in St. Anthony with no shoes, no vehicles, his house completely destroyed behind him, and he had no place to stay. He said he waited and waited before someone finally found him a pair of shoes. When he went back to his ranch the next day there was nothing left; his house, his cattle, and all his pens and sheds were destroyed.

The last thought I have to share is that early on in the process of building the dam I remember discussions about why this was going to be an earthen fill dam instead of concrete. It came down to simple math—the cost-benefit analysis did not justify concrete. And so it was built as it was.[2]

PERSONAL REFLECTIONS

The collapse of the dam caught our attention in Pocatello but posed no threat since the Snake River was well to the west and lower in elevation. I had relatives who lived in the path of the water, but by Saturday evening, we'd heard they were all safe. So it appeared that the failure of the dam had nothing to do with me.

But the next day in church as I was teaching a Sunday School lesson on the virtues of service, a knock sounded on the door. Our leaders were asking for volunteers to sandbag along the Snake River in Idaho Falls. After changing our clothes, we carpooled 50 miles north to help out.

Wow, I thought. *This is probably the best lesson on service I'll ever give.*

I made the trip to Idaho Falls sitting on a pile of empty sandbags in the back of a pickup truck, along with a group of my friends. Our work gloves and shovels were at the ready. It was a sunny summer day, and there was a sense of adventure in the air.

However. the sense of adventure quickly turned to anxiety when we reached the west bank of the Snake River in downtown Idaho Falls.

---

2.   Live interview with Jim Roker, June 2015.

I had always loved looking at the long bank of waterfalls, where, on average days, the river dropped perhaps fifty feet along a long line of lava flows. It was a serene sight. But this was not a typical day, and the falls were completely inundated by the sheer volume of water roaring down the narrow river channel. It looked like the river was entirely free flowing with no falls at all. The roar this volume of water created made the hair stand up on the back of my neck, particularly since the water was moving so fast.

As soon as we arrived at our assigned spot, local government officials put us to work, with some filling sandbags and others placing them on a growing wall along the riverbank. Across the street were numerous businesses and hotels that needed protection from the flood. It was difficult work, but the urgency of the situation was so evident that we took sandbags as quickly as they were sent forward. It was remarkable how quickly the wall grew to more than two miles in length.

While it felt great to be doing something so useful, it soon became evident that in spite of our best efforts, the river was rising faster than we could hold it back. When we had first started, the river was at least four or five feet below us. But as the hours passed, the level kept rising until it was lapping at the base of the small wall of sand we had built. In these extreme circumstances, we hurried even faster. But when the surging water was just six inches below the top of the sandbags, getting us wet each time we placed a new bag, we were ordered to abandon the project. It was, quite frankly, terrifying to see that much water flowing by us at what seemed a hundred miles an hour, and just inches in front of us. There was a very real danger that our sandbag wall would be over-topped at any moment.

Racing back to the truck, parked farther up the hill, we turned and watched as the river continued to rise up and over our pathetic line of sandbags. The businesses across the street were doomed to be flooded. The next step for Idaho Falls was to dig a trench around the Broadway Bridge just south of where we'd been working in hopes of saving the bridge from destruction.

Realizing there was nothing more we could do in Idaho Falls, we loaded back into the pickup trucks and made our way south. We turned off at the Rose Exit of I-15, where local leaders hoped we could sandbag the headgates to a large diversion canal that sent water out to the potato fields. It was here that I came face-to-face with an even older fear: the Old Rose Bridge. It lay directly in the path of the raging water, with debris crashing into its superstructure. Old fears gripped me.

Within sight of where we started sandbagging, I could see the steel frame of the Old Rose Bridge, which crossed the Snake River north of Blackfoot, Idaho. As a child, that bridge had terrified me each time we crossed it. The reason is that while the steel truss skeleton seemed sturdy enough, the deck was made of wood planks that made a distinct clicking sound as our car passed over them. To me, it seemed impossible that wood could be strong enough to hold up a car. The lifting and dropping of the planks as the car wheels crossed between the end of one plank and the beginning of the next convinced me that we were going to fall through at any moment. No amount of assurance from my parents could persuade me otherwise, which is why I was so relieved a few years before the flood when they built a new prestressed concrete bridge just north of the Old Rose Bridge, closing the old structure to vehicle traffic. I had actually gone to the trouble of driving out to the old bridge so I could walk across it to convince myself I'd been foolish as a child. But at this point in the bridge's existence, many of the wood planks had gaping holes in them, through which I could see the river flowing swiftly below. I was still rather traumatized. Now, standing just downstream from my old nemesis, I could see that the force of water piling up against its center pier and actually surging against the deck itself put the structure in danger. I worried that my fears of the bridge failing could actually come true. But there was nothing that could be done, so I worked as quickly as I could with the others to protect the massive headgates.

Once again, the river was proving itself more than our equal. When we first started at this site, the water was well below the concrete platform on which we stood. But after just an hour or two of work, the water had risen to the lower level of our sand wall, and once again we were forced to abandon the project. It was dark then, and the glow of lights on the undulating surface of the raging water was awesome. We went home exhausted, not knowing if our labor had helped at all.

A THOROUGHBRED ARABIAN

The next Saturday, my mother asked if I would go with her to Rexburg to help dig mud out of my aunt Jeanette Burnside's rental house.

At this point, we had been exposed to a full week of news about the path of destruction the flood had left in its wake. One of my favorite memories was watching a television advertisement that asserted "Boise-Cascade homes are built like a ship." The very next scene on the news was that of a Boise-Cascade home literally floating down Main Street in Rexburg, having been torn loose from its foundations by the force of the flood. It was, indeed, behaving like a ship. It even turned the corner from State Street to Main Street.

We drove to Rexburg, where the city proper was in ruins. Debris had piled up against anything that was strong enough to resist the current, including my aunt's brick rental home. The basement of the house was filled with four feet of foul-smelling mud that took a full day's work to haul out. We formed a bucket brigade to move this sludge up and out. The water had reached more than six feet high on the walls of the main floor, and everything was water-logged and soaked through, including plaster and light fixtures.

As we worked, we heard the astonishing story of how my aunt and uncle received word of the flood out on their farm five miles north of Rexburg and one mile from the Teton River, through which the flood roared. I confirmed her recollections in a live interview in June 2015.

On the morning of June 5, the Bureau of Reclamation sent word to local law enforcement and the sheriff's office that people below the dam should start to evacuate.

When my aunt and uncle heard the news, they went outside to see what the commotion was all about. My uncle Charles said that at first it seemed like people were overreacting. He felt they'd have more than enough time to load up the chinchillas he raised, as well as load up the pure-bred Arabian horses he loved to train.

"But when we looked upstream, we could see the progress of the wall of water coming toward our farm by watching the telephone poles snap when the water hit them."

That brought the reality of the danger home very quickly, and they knew they had to get out of the way fast if they were to have any chance of surviving.

So, relinquishing any hope of saving the chinchilla or other animals, my uncle went out to the corral and opened the gate to let out his one-year-old prized Arabian colt. Slapping it on the back haunches, he sent the horse running while he and my aunt climbed into the car and drove toward the nearest high spot.

The story of the horse is truly remarkable. As the towering wall of water, perhaps thirty to forty feet high at this point, approached the farm, the horse started running for his life. Shortly after this, a news helicopter flying overhead spotted the horse moving ahead of the water. The crew watched in amazement as this healthy young animal, bred for endurance, raced for more than five miles, jumping fences, racing around haystacks, and jumping over creeks. Behind it the water swamped and killed countless cows and other livestock and smashed houses and outbuildings. Ultimately the young Arabian managed to work itself to the outer edge of the advancing water and up onto a small hill that was quickly surrounded by water but not overtopped. My uncle later recovered the animal but said, "It lost all its training—it had been so terrified that it forgot everything." He said this with tears coming down his cheeks and a sense of pride in his voice at the power and grace of this animal he loved.

My family spent days working in Rexburg. My aunt and uncle and cousins spent months. But the house we worked so hard to clear of mud and debris was eventually declared unlivable. Like most buildings left standing by the flood, it was razed. The buildings on my aunt and uncle's farm were completely destroyed, having been close to the natural channel of the Teton River. But fortunately no one in our family was killed or injured, and the time we spent working together became an important part of the fabric of our family life.

As to the Old Rose Bridge, I saw it lying in a heap in the middle of the river, torn from its moorings by the force of the water. I felt an electric shock to have a childhood fear played out in my lifetime, even if for a different reason than my original apprehension. On the other hand, the new bridge had weathered the flood and is still in service today.

Today, few remnants of the flood remain to remind us of those remarkable days in 1976. Idahoans are resilient. Hopefully we learned lessons to prevent new tragedies as men work to turn nature from its natural course.

SOURCES

1. *Tragedy: A Chronology of the Teton Dam Disaster.* Bulletin Publishing Co, Inc., Blackfoot, Idaho. June 11, 1976 (original copy provided to the author by his aunt, Jeanette Burnside, a survivor of the flood).

2. *The Standard Journal* (newspaper). Rexburg, Idaho. Various, including 7-28-1976, 8-11-1976, 9-7-1976.

3. *Images of America, The Teton Dam Disaster*. Dylan J. McDonald. Arcadia Publishing. Charleston, South Carolina. 2006.

4. Bureau of Reclamation, Pacific Northwest Region, Idaho. www.usbr.gov/pn/about/Teton.html.

5. *The Em-Kayan Magazine*. December 1974. Volume 33, Number 10. Published by Morrison-Knudsen Company, Inc. Syms-York Co. Boise, Idaho.

6. *The Em-Kayan Magazine*. December 1975. Volume 34, Number 10. Published by Morrison-Knudsen Company, Inc. Syms-York Co. Boise, Idaho.

7. "Teton Dam." Wikipedia, the Free Encyclopedia. Wikimedia Foundation, Inc. 12 April 2015. 18 April 2015. http://en.wikipedia.org/wiki/Teton_Dam.

8. Original interview with Jim Roker, Rigby, Idaho. June 2015.

CORNELIUS VANDERBILT

CHAPTER 5

VANDERBILT GOES TO WAR

Cornelius Vanderbilt was a self-made multimillionaire who dominated the American economy in the nineteenth century, becoming the wealthiest man in the country. At the height of his success, Vanderbilt controlled one out of every twenty dollars in circulation—an accumulation of wealth that has never since been equaled. He made his first fortune in shipping, starting out by transferring cargo in sailboats from Staten Island, New York, to Manhattan Island. An early adopter of steamships, Vanderbilt eventually monopolized trade on the Hudson River. He then used ocean-going steamships to underbid all the competitors on the New York–to–San Francisco route (via land transfer in Panama) until he drove competing lines into bankruptcy. He was so bold in his competition that other lines paid him substantial royalties to stay out of their region—payments for doing nothing! Eventually he even underbid the hugely profitable U.S. mail transatlantic route between the U.S., Britain, and Europe. Ordinary people saw him as a hero since he brought the cost of steamship tickets down by more than 80 percent in many markets, making steamship travel affordable. Others saw the deplorable conditions on his bargain-basement ships as bordering on inhumane and not worthy of a gentleman.

In time, Vanderbilt made the bulk of his great fortune in railroads as he squashed all competition into submission using monopolistic combinations that formed the famous New York Central line. Today, the two most visible reminders of Vanderbilt's power are the magnificent Grand Central Station in New York City that he commissioned at the height of his fame and power, and his endowment of Vanderbilt University in Nashville, Tennessee.

But along the way is a story about Cornelius Vanderbilt that seems out of character for the ruthless capitalist. It took place in the early days of the Civil War, when his patriotism came to the fore. This highly competitive tycoon set personal interests aside to help the Northern States forge one of its most important weapons against the Confederacy—the naval blockade of Southern ports.

As a War-Between-the-States seemed increasingly likely, most merchants in New York were frantic to prevent it. Cotton was their most profitable commodity, representing fully two-thirds of U.S. exports, and losing that trade as a result of war would be costly. Some even went so far as to declare that if the South seceded, New York State should join them. But from the beginning, Cornelius Vanderbilt favored the Union.

In early 1861, after war was declared, the federal government began chartering (leasing) ships to aid the Union cause. Vanderbilt was infuriated by the government-mandated commission these brokers collected to facilitate these transactions. He thought it immoral for them to take a profit, given the desperate needs of the U.S. Navy. Plus, Vanderbilt felt that the price the U.S. Treasury paid to lease commercial vessels was exorbitant, even though he and others were responsible for providing both crews and operating costs. Although he would have accepted lower payments, the U.S. Navy said they had to pay him the going rate or explain why other shipping lines charged more than Vanderbilt.

Vanderbilt's proposed solution was to sell his largest and most powerful vessels, including the incomparable steamer *Vanderbilt* to the U.S. Navy. The *Vanderbilt* was the largest ship afloat in the United States and had the most up-to-date steam engines. To make sure the price was fair, he agreed to let three men holding the rank of Commodore or higher set the price. This would assure that he wouldn't personally profit from the transaction. Then, before the sale occurred, Vanderbilt made a surprising offer, writing that "if this will not answer, will the government accept the *Vanderbilt* as a present from their humble servant?" This was an astonishing offer, given that the *Vanderbilt* cost more than

1 million dollars to build.[1] It was a generous act unmatched by any other and motivated out of sincere patriotism.

But the secretary of the navy, Gideon Welles, refused the offer with no explanation. So the navy continued to charter Vanderbilt's ships at great expense. No one knows why Welles refused since he didn't even bother to write a reply.

The key to understanding this story is the fact that President Lincoln had ordered a blockade of all Southern ports to prevent war material, such as ammunition and cannons, from going into the Confederacy. The blockade also seized outbound shipments of cotton that could otherwise provide a source of money to the rebellious states. The Confederacy's only real chance of winning the war was to defeat this blockade so they could get war supplies from Europe, having limited industrial capacity of their own.

THE BATTLE OF HAMPTON ROADS

The blockade continued until March 1862. On March 8, a new type of ship emerged at Hampton Roads, near Norfolk, Virginia. The Confederate ship *Merrimac* had been damaged above the waterline in battle but had been found seaworthy below the damage, including full serviceability of her steam engines. The Confederacy struck upon the bold idea of building a new upper works that was completely protected by iron armor plate. In some respects, it looked like a long triangular lean-to, with ports that opened on each side from which the cannons could fire. The ship was hefty and lacked maneuverability, but the iron plate made it almost invincible to enemy gunfire.

Once completed, the ship was renamed the Confederate States ship (CSS) *Virginia*. It stunned the Union Navy when the newly commissioned ironclad ship steamed out into Hampton Roads at the mouth of the James River, where it proceeded to sink two large Union ships. *Virginia* fired first on the United States ship (USS) *Cumberland* and then rammed it into submission. It then turned its guns on the *USS Congress*, a frigate, which ran aground as a result of the furious fusillade from the *Virginia*. The

---

1. $1,000,000 in 1861 equals approximately $27,000,000 in 2016, according to DaveManual.com inflation calculator, although the cost of building a ship comparable in size to the *Vanderbilt* today would cost many hundreds of millions of dollars. Vanderbilt was willing put this investment at risk.

THE *MERRIMAC* IN DRY DOCK BEING RETROFIT AS THE IRON CLAD C.S.S. *VIRGINIA*

Congress surrendered, which caused the *Virginia* to stand aside until Union shore batteries opened up on the CSS *Virginia*. This violation of military protocol so infuriated the commander of the *Virginia* that he ordered his ship back to work, firing on the *Congress* until the stricken ship was entirely consumed by fire. This fire blazed in the darkness, a bold symbol of the Confederacy's new maritime power. Planners in Washington D.C. were terrified by both the loss of two ships and the adverse press the image of the ship burning in the harbor generated. This group included Secretary Welles, a member of Lincoln's cabinet. Of this incident, Welles said, "I called at once on the President, who had sent for me. Several members of the Cabinet soon gathered. Stanton (War Secretary) was already there, and there was general excitement and alarm." Welles later said that the secretary of war was "almost frantic . . . . The *Merrimac* (*Virginia*) he said would destroy every vessel in the service, could lay every city on the coast under contribution, could take Fortress Monroe." He continued. "McLellan's mistaken purpose of advancing on Richmond, Virginia by the Peninsula must be abandoned." Welles also said that both Lincoln and Stanton repeatedly went to the windows of the White House to look out on the Potomac to see if the *Merrimack* might not be advancing on Washington D.C. He concluded by saying that "Stanton was the most frightened man I ever saw."[2]

U.S.S. *CONGRESS*

Clearly, the iron plate was about to change the course of war forever. The immediate answer to the first battle at Hampton Roads was for the U.S. Navy to tow their own new ironclad, the USS *Monitor*, from Brooklyn, New York, to the James River. The *Monitor* engaged the *Virginia* in battle the following day.

The *Monitor* had a very different design from the *Virginia* in that it was smaller than the Confederate ship and had a single rotating metal turret from which two cannons fired. Far more maneuverable, it was able to circle, dodge, and feint at the *Virginia* with both ships firing on each other. At the end of the day, both ships had been damaged, but both remained afloat and battle worthy. The captain of the *Virginia* ordered her back up the river to the safety of the Gosport Naval Yard in Norfolk, Virginia, expecting there would be future battles.

This is where Vanderbilt comes into the story. Out of a desperate fear that this new "monster" could destroy the blockade, Secretary of War Stanton sent a telegram to Vanderbilt. He asked how much Vanderbilt would charge to either destroy the *Virginia* or at least bottle it up in port. Rather than reply by telegram, Vanderbilt boarded a private train

---

2. *The First Tycoon, The Epic Life of Cornelius Vanderbilt*. T.J. Stiles. 2009. Alfred A. Knopf, a division of Random House, Inc., New York, 342. Portions of this quote are also found in steelnavy.com, http://steelnavy.com/FlagshipVirginia.htm (accessed February 3, 2016).

THE *MONITOR* AND *MERRIMAC* BY J. O. DAVIDSON

to Washington, where he immediately went to the White House to meet with Stanton and Lincoln. Author T. J. Styles, Vanderbilt's biographer, described the meeting. Note that Vanderbilt was informally called the Commodore because of his large fleet of ships:

> Lincoln asked if Vanderbilt could do anything to keep the enemy vessel from steaming out of Norfolk once more. "I replied to him," the Commodore wrote, "that it was my opinion that if the steamship *Vanderbilt* was there properly manned, the *Merrimac (Virginia)* would not venture to come out; or if she did, that the chances were ten to one that the *Vanderbilt* would sink and destroy her." Then the president asked his price. "I at once informed Mr. Lincoln that I was determined that I would not allow myself to do anything by

INSPECTION OF DAMAGE OF *MONITOR* AFTER HER FIGHT WITH THE *MERRIMAC*.

which I could be ranked with the herd of thieves and vampires who were fattening off the Government by means of army contracts." Vanderbilt recalled that "I had no vessels to sell or bargains to make, except one." He would give the *Vanderbilt* to the government on the condition that he, the Commodore, should control its preparations for battle. Lincoln replied, "I accept her."[3]

Thus, it was, that Cornelius Vanderbilt donated his greatest ship to the Union cause, putting it at risk of destruction from the powerful Southern ironclad. Vanderbilt immediately had a large armored ram built and attached to the bow of his ship and then went with it to the James River. He did this in just four days!

The ship's great size and speed meant it could attack the *Virginia* quickly, smashing into the smaller vessel with such force that it would be overturned and sunk. The chance to do that came just once as the *Virginia* tentatively emerged from the river into the harbor. The Union *Monitor* was waiting at the mouth, and the *Vanderbilt* and another navy ship, the *Minnesota*, were ready to ram her. Seeing this, the *Virginia* retreated back to Norfolk, never to come out again. Vanderbilt's prediction

3.   Ibid. 346.

U.S.S. *Vanderbilt*

came true, and he successfully protected the blockade from this new threat. When Union troops invaded Norfolk later that year, the Confederacy scuttled the *Virginia*, setting it on fire so it would not fall into enemy hands. Vanderbilt had won his first naval battle without a shot being fired.

VANDERBILT PROCUREMENTS

Once the *Virginia* threat was ended, Vanderbilt returned to New York to continue his business activities. But his service to the Union was not yet finished. The secretary of war had gained such confidence in Vanderbilt's skill that he asked him to negotiate charters on behalf of the United States. He was also to supervise inspections of the ships brought into government service to make sure they lived up to the terms of their agreements. As a proven hard negotiator, Vanderbilt was perfectly suited for this task. One U.S. naval officer later said he estimated Vanderbilt saved the government more than 50 percent on each of the contracts he negotiated. Vanderbilt used all his skills in this endeavor, including appeals to patriotism, his influence as a major shipper, and his broad knowledge of the trade.

Another way Vanderbilt supported the Union cause was in outfitting his ships, at his own expense, to provide convoy escort duty for merchant ships bound to and from Panama. This is the route they used to bring large gold reserves from California to the U.S. Treasury. The blockade of southern ports had been instituted just weeks after the outbreak of war, but in the first two or three years of the war, it was only marginally successful. Nearly two out of three merchant ships made their way through the blockade into Mobile, New Orleans, Galveston, and other southern ports. But as more and more Union ships came into service, the success of the blockade runners was choked off to little more than a trickle. The effect on the Confederate economy was paralyzing.

Vanderbilt also used his own ships to address the threat of commerce raiders. A commerce raider was different from a blockade runner. Blockade runners operated cargo ships that tried to sneak in and out of southern ports. Commerce raiders were pirates who captured cargo vessels in Atlantic waters and even as far away as the Indian Ocean to commandeer their cargoes and demand ransom from the ship owners. If a vessel failed to submit, the raiders sank it. Eventually the superior strength of the Union Navy brought the raiders to heel. But before that occurred, the *Vanderbilt* prevented many acts of piracy. Just having this powerful ship in the vicinity was enough for raiders to call off an attack and retreat to poorly defended waters.

So Cornelius Vanderbilt's contribution to the Union cause in the Civil War was three-fold:

CORNELIUS VANDERBILT

1. He helped bottle up the *Virginia* during a critical time.

2. He brought business discipline and strict honesty to the procurement process.

3. He donated ships and crews at his own expense to fend off southern commerce raiders and protect vital transit routes.

Today, Cornelius Vanderbilt is primarily remembered for the university he endowed and his business prowess. His great business enterprises have long since passed into other hands, and the Vanderbilt fortune has been disbursed. But his willingness to risk a great part of his fortune on behalf of the United States government is a forgotten story of U.S. history that deserves remembrance.

PERSONAL CONNECTION

I first came across Cornelius Vanderbilt while researching a book I was writing about a fictional British family who wanted to emigrate to the United States from England in the mid-1850s. The book is entitled *Steamship to Zion*. Their ultimate destination was to be the Nevada-Utah area far into the interior of the Mountain West. While many immigrants traveled by wagon train to the west, my research revealed that the most common route to California from the East Coast in 1850 was by steamship to Panama. After that ocean journey, travelers used donkeys to cross the fifty-mile Isthmus of Panama. Once on the Pacific shore, they either sailed or steamed to San Francisco, which was the closest port to where gold was discovered in 1849. Vanderbilt came into the trade when tens of thousands of fortune seekers wanted to get to California as fast as possible.

In many ways, Vanderbilt was the *Southwest Airlines* of his times. Monopolies that charged high fares for high-quality accommodations ran the first steamships to Panama on both its Atlantic and Pacific shores. Vanderbilt saw an opportunity to undercut their price. His discounted fares to Panama were 80 percent lower than his competitors'. Of course other lines moved to match his price, but he almost single-handedly made transportation to the West Coast affordable for almost everyone. Soon his ships were crammed full of fortune seekers and all the merchants who supported them. It was his Panama route that opened the vast lands of California and the Pacific Northwest.

But travel on a Vanderbilt ship was grueling. The discounted fares meant terrible food, crowded conditions, and little support when a person arrived in Panama. But since the Forty-Niners wanted to get to the gold fields as quickly as possible, they endured these inconveniences.

After learning about Vanderbilt's discounted fares through Panama, I decided to have my fictional family get to the Mountain West by way of San Francisco rather than by wagon train from Nebraska. This gave an unusual twist to the story.

To adequately describe what they encountered on such a journey, my wife and I booked a cruise through the Caribbean to Panama, where our ship made its way through the first locks of the Panama Canal. Once in Lake Gatun, we got off the vessel and boarded an excursion train that took us to the Pacific Coast. On the Atlantic side, Panama is a tropical jungle, and on the Pacific side, there is a California-style desert. The unique desert landscape was familiar to us since we are West Coast people. This excursion gave me the insight to finish my story in a realistic way. While our cruise was far more comfortable than a Vanderbilt steamship, I still appreciated that it was his vision that opened California to the world—and this just ten years before he played such an important role in helping the Union win the Civil War.

SOURCES

1. *The First Tycoon, the Epic Life of Cornelius Vanderbilt.* T.J. Stiles. 2009. Alfred A. Knopf, a division of Random House, Inc., New York.

2. "CSS *Virginia*." Wikipedia, the Free Encyclopedia. www.en.wipedia.org Article CSS Virginia.

3. "CSS *Alabama*." *The Encyclopedia of Alabama*. www.encylopediaofalabama.org Article H-973.

The celebration at Promontory Point on the completion of
the Transcontinental Railroad

CHAPTER 6

THE FINAL PUSH OF THE UNION PACIFIC

Early in his presidency, on July 1, 1862, Abraham Lincoln signed the Pacific Railway Act to incorporate the Union Pacific Railroad and Telegraph Company (UP). This act gave UP the authority to construct a road across public lands from Nebraska to the western border of Nevada. To finance such an unprecedented undertaking, the new company was granted the power of eminent domain to legally take the land needed to build the railroad. It was also given ownership of five alternating sections of land per mile of rail laid. This was a land grant on an astonishing scale. In addition, the government would reimburse the company up to $1.25 per acre for land claimed by eminent domain. In other words, the government gave the land to the company, as well as the freedom to develop or sell it, and then paid them up to $1.25 for each acre it gave them! This was a direct subsidy to help cover the cost of building the railroad, making it the largest vote of public expenditures in U.S. history.

The primary goal of the act was to weld the Pacific Coast territories to the rest of the country, but with the outbreak of the Civil War, controversy surrounded it. Passage of the act when southern representatives couldn't vote because they were in rebellion made it clear that Lincoln and Congress intended to secure a northern route to keep slavery out of the western territories.

It was remarkable for the government to undertake such a project while simultaneously arming for war. The demands the Civil War placed on the Union precluded the use of many of the engineers and laborers it would take to build the railroad. That was one reason it took seven years to complete the two railroads to Promontory Point in the desolate plains of Northern Utah.

But the act was also a gesture to the world that the United States was always to be united by the most modern technology possible.[1]

Skeptics believed that this particular railroad could never be built because of the many physical obstacles in the way of its completion. These included carving a path through hostile Indian territories, as well as grading and tunneling through the Wasatch Mountains in Utah and the Sierra-Nevada Mountains of Nevada and Northern California. But it was just such a bold gesture that Lincoln wanted to make, hoping it would convince an anxious public that in spite of the war, the country was still on the right track.

Since the California portion of the railroad would be far harder to build because of numerous mountains requiring many tunnels and enormous amounts of grading, the Central Pacific Railroad (CP) was separately incorporated. The CP's task was to traverse the Sierra-Nevada Mountains and meet the UP somewhere in Nevada or Utah. Government subsidies for the Central Pacific were much larger since the construction cost per mile was significantly greater.

When the two railroads met, there was, in the words of noted historian Stephen Ambrose, "Nothing like it in the world!" a title he gave his book. A stagecoach journey from Boston to San Francisco that took more than a month at a cost of $1,000 was reduced to just seven days at a fare of $65 by rail. Freight rates dropped by a similar magnitude. Dangerous maritime passages via Panama or Cape Horn were no longer needed, and the vast resources of the American midwest, mountain states, and coastal areas were made available to every citizen at a reasonable cost. The

---

1.   It set a precedent that was followed later in our history, including during the Great Depression when enormous public resources were devoted to rural electrification (bringing electricity to remote farms in all regions of the country). It occurred in 1935 when public funds were used to build the Hoover Dam to "reclaim" the states of the southwest by making water and electricity available from the Colorado River. All these projects were logical successors to the Pacific Railway Act.

transcontinental railroad was truly a turning point in history, increasing the wealth of the United States and firmly establishing it as a two-ocean world power.

What is not generally known, except to those who have studied the building of the railroad, is the crucial role Brigham Young and the Latter-day Saint settlers of Utah played in its completion. It fell to them to finish the line through some of its most difficult and challenging sections. In fact, when Stephen Ambrose was asked what his biggest surprise was in researching the building of the transcontinental railroad, he replied, "That's easy. Brigham Young." When pressed for more detail, he said, "I had no idea what an efficient and dynamic leader Brigham Young was. The way he organized his people to help finish the Union Pacific Railroad was remarkable. In my view if he had not acted as a religious leader, he had the capacity to be President of the United States or a Prime Minister of England or another European power."[2] This is high praise from the biographer of Dwight D. Eisenhower and the founder of the World War II Museum in New Orleans.

It is the story of this final phase of building the railroad when labor was scarce and the demands of the project were greatest that has been forgotten in U.S. history. But it is important to first understand the background of Brigham Young and the Latter-day Saint pioneers who followed him to the remote mountain valleys of Utah and Idaho.

BRIGHAM YOUNG

Brigham Young was a highly controversial person in his day. A glazier by trade, he was an enthusiastic convert to The Church of Jesus Christ of Latter-day Saints soon after reading the Book of Mormon. He became a close friend of the Prophet Joseph Smith Jr. and succeeded to the presidency of the Church when Joseph was murdered in Carthage, Illinois, by an anti-Mormon mob.

In 1846, the Latter-day Saints were forced to abandon their homes in Illinois and migrate beyond the boundaries of the United States. They ultimately settled in the Mexican Territory they called Deseret (later

---

2.   Stephen Ambrose speaking at the University of Utah shortly after completing *Nothing Like It in the World*. I attended this lecture and recorded this statement because it was such an unexpected answer to the question. He confirms this assessment in *Nothing Like It in the World*. Stephen Ambrose. 2000. Touchstone Books, Simon & Schuster, 278.

Brigham Young

named Utah) so they could be left alone in their remote mountain wilderness to freely practice their religion and rebuild their lives.

After the Mexican-American War, in which the Latter-day Saints' Mormon Battalion played a crucial role, President Millard Fillmore appointed Brigham Young to be the first governor of the Utah Territory. But by 1857, relations between the Church and the U.S. government had soured once again. The Saints were practicing polygamy, and the U.S. in general (but more particularly the Republican Party at that time) considered its practice one of the twin relics of barbarism—the other being slavery. To the Mormons, however, it was a commandment from God.

By 1858, President James Buchanan was persuaded on false grounds that Brigham Young's religious dominance of the Utah Territory posed enough of a threat to democracy in the region that he dispatched General Albert Sidney Johnston, with a large contingent of the U.S. Army, to impose order on the territory. This outraged the Latter-day Saints, who felt perfectly capable of managing their own affairs, so they used guerrilla tactics to slow the advance of the army. Mormon parties harassed the army in Wyoming and deprived them of provisions during the hard winter months. This resistance became known as the Utah War.

When Johnston's army finally made its way into Salt Lake City, they found the city abandoned. The Saints were so opposed to the military's presence that they had filled every house with loose straw so they could burn the town to the ground rather than submit to martial law.

Fortunately President Buchanan finally appointed a peace commission, and after meeting with Brigham Young and other Church leaders, they struck a compromise with which General Johnston carefully complied. Consequently, the army did not engage in military action, but Johnston did establish a permanent military outpost at Camp Floyd to the southwest of Salt Lake City. Order was restored, and the tentative relationship between the Utah Saints and the rest of the United States was reestablished on peaceful terms. Polygamy, however, remained a sore point.

In 1868, when the Union Pacific Railroad was approaching the eastern borders of the Utah territory and the Central Pacific was making its way east from Nevada toward the western border, rank-and-file Mormons were conflicted. On the one hand they wished to keep their relative isolation, but on the other hand, in order to prosper, they needed trade with the outside world.

YOUNG IS ENTHUSIASTIC

Many in the political establishment assumed Brigham Young would oppose a railroad through the Utah Territory since it would open the land to outsiders. But in fact, Brigham Young was enthusiastic about the railroad connecting Utah to the rest of the world and even purchased shares of UP stock when it was first made available to the public. He met personally with Grenville Dodge, the lead engineer for the UP, to discuss surveys and to urge a route that would bring the railroad right through Salt Lake City.

Young had several motives for this support. First, it would make it easier for Latter-day Saint immigrants from England to make their way to Utah, incurring a much lower cost, both in terms of money and personal hardship, than traveling by wagon train or handcart. Second, it would open markets in the eastern states to Utah farm produce while allowing easier transport of finished goods into the territory. Finally, even in those early days, Brigham recognized that tourism to the magnificent Wasatch Mountains and the natural wonder of the Great Salt Lake would be a great economic boon to the area. The Latter-day Saints needed cash and trade in their growing communities.

But Brigham's early efforts to influence the railroad had little effect until the rails reached Evanston, Wyoming, on the Utah border. At this point, the Union Pacific and the Central Pacific were in an all-out construction war with each other. Both companies were anxious to build track as far west (UP) or as far east (CP) as possible before Congress declared the final meeting point. As already mentioned, each mile of track laid resulted in a direct cash payment to the company, as well as the grant of substantial amounts of real estate, so the railroad company with the most miles would end up with the greatest profit.

Thus, when the competing railroads reached the borders of Utah, they needed qualified workers to lay tracks. It wasn't just the money that turned the railroads to the Latter-day Saints for help. Their existing workers were increasingly abandoning the project to return home, and because Utah was about as far from civilization as anyone could get in 1868, replacements were hard to come by. Plus, they needed these new workers in a hurry to set the meeting point of the two railroads in the most financially favorable location.

Both parties thought of striking a deal with Brigham Young for labor. Thomas Durant, the owner of the UP, sent a telegram to Brigham Young in May 1868, asking if he was interested in entering into a contract to complete grading work through the Wasatch Mountains to the valley floor of the Great Salt Lake. This included an offer for Brigham to name his price. Brigham replied immediately in the affirmative.[3]

He set his terms, which included free rail transportation for any Latter-day Saint emigrants then en route from England who were willing to work on the railroad project. Thomas accepted, and Brigham immediately sent out a call to area congregations to send as many able-bodied men as possible to work on the grading and tunneling projects. Within a month, work was underway in Echo Canyon, to the east of Ogden, Utah. But in spite of Thomas's generous offer, Brigham was personally financing all work while he awaited cash payments from the Union Pacific in New York.

The UP was pretty good about getting supplies and equipment to the more-than-three-thousand-man workforce since no work could be done without shovels, picks, nitroglycerin (blasting for four tunnels), food, and water. But it was always slow to send money for payroll.

Many of Brigham's critics thought he intended to exploit his own people by signing a profitable contract and then hiring his religious followers for a pittance. But as already mentioned, Brigham tapped out his personal

3.   *Nothing Like It in the World*, 283.

finances to make payments to the laborers while desperately awaiting reimbursement from the Union Pacific. At one point, he advanced more than $130,000 of his personal funds, but the UP sent just $100,000 in payment.

Still, the Saints worked around the clock on both the grading and tunneling through the hard granite mountains. They burned great piles of sagebrush at night to provide light to the workers so they could keep going, providing some of the best grading, tunneling, and roadbed preparation in the entire system.

At this point, the Central Pacific was desperate. Leland Stanford pleaded with Brigham for additional workers to supplement the Chinese workers the CP was using to blast the many tunnels through the Sierra-Nevada Mountains. Now, nearly 700 miles east of San Francisco, it was hard to get workers to lay the track in the high Utah desert and salt flats. Finally, Brigham sent word to bishops, asking for more men.

Eventually Stanford succeeded in getting Brigham to sign a contract with the Central Pacific to grade across the desert north of the Great Salt Lake toward Ogden. The work was grueling and relentless, but men who had previously been unemployed relished the chance to earn an income—especially since their prophet-leader promised them it would be good for Utah and the Church in the long run.

As the arduous work drew to its finish, the two railroads continued competing. If it hadn't been so expensive, it would almost be humorous. For example, consider the folly that when the two roads met in the desert west of Ogden, they kept grading past each other for many miles because Congress had failed to name the specific meeting point at which subsidies would end; hence, each road was billing the government for the duplicate track. The CP wanted Congress to specify Ogden as the official meeting point, the largest population center west of Omaha. The UP wanted to meet somewhere in Nevada. Finally Congress stepped in and declared that Promontory Point on the west Utah desert would be the official termination point for each line.

As an interesting note, the train that brought Thomas Durant to Promontory was held up on May 6 by angry workers who demanded payment. Taking Thomas and UP director John Duff as hostages, they demanded their pay, saying they would not let them go until $200,000 had been sent forward. To emphasize the point, they chained his car to the siding. Thomas offered to telegraph for the money but instead requested a

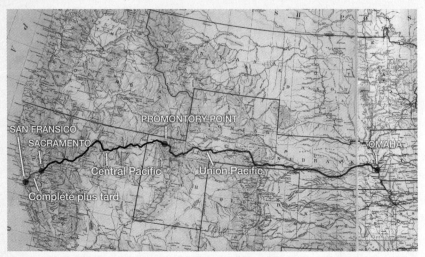

Map of the Union Pacific and Central Pacific Railroads; they join at Promontory Point northwest of Salt Lake City

detachment of the U.S. Army to be sent from Fort Bridger. This was done, but the troop train didn't stop at the right place. Other officers of the UP eventually intervened, and money was sent forward so Thomas could be ransomed. A reporter for the *San Francisco Bulletin* said Thomas paid some $235,000 in back wages.[4] His train was released, and he continued on to the joining ceremony.

On May 10, 1869, the official ceremony was held at Promontory when Leland Stanford swung a pick to drive the golden spike into the last rail that joined the two lines. The telegraphist at the spot ignored the fact that he missed hitting the spike, sending out in the coded electric signal to the rest of the country that the rails had been joined. Recognizing the significance of the event, the Liberty Bell was pealed in Philadelphia, 200 cannons were fired in San Francisco, and parades and celebrations were held throughout the country. Even cities in the former Confederate States shared in the celebration. Truly, something remarkable had been accomplished.[5] Even some of the wounds of the Civil War started to heal as ambitious young men and women from both north and south began making their way west to find their fortunes.

---

4   Ibid., 359–360.
5   Ibid.

GRENVILLE M. DODGE REFLECTS ON THE CEREMONY AT PROMONTORY

The following excerpt is an excellent description of the significance of the joining of the two railroads. Colonel Grenville M. Dodge, chief engineer of the Union Pacific, delivered it on the fortieth anniversary of the driving of the golden spike.

The building of a Pacific steam road to connect the streams flowing into the Atlantic and Pacific was advocated as early as 1819 before a mile of the railroad was built in any part of the world. It took practical form when Asa Whitney, in 1845, in petitioning Congress in behalf of the Pacific Railroad, said: "You will see that it will change the whole world." Senator Thomas H. Benton in 1849 pleaded that the great line when built should "be adorned with its crowning honor, the colossal statue of the great Columbus, whose design it accomplishes, hewn from the granite mass of a peak of the Rocky Mountains, overlooking the road, the mountain itself the pedestal, and the statue a part of the mountain, pointing with outstretched arm to the western horizon, and saying to the flying passenger, 'There is the East! There is India!'"

Charles Sumner in 1853 said: "The railroad from the Atlantic to the Pacific, traversing a whole continent and binding together two oceans, this mighty thoroughfare when completed will mark an epoch of human progress second only to that of our Declaration of Independence. May the day soon come!" And it did come, and all the prophecies were fulfilled when the first transcontinental line was completed and the tracks joined at Promontory Point, Utah, on May 10, 1869, just forty years ago.

This ceremony was one of peace and harmony between the Union Pacific, coming from the east, and the Central Pacific, coming from the west. For a year or more there had been great contention and rivalry between the two companies, the Union Pacific endeavoring to reach Humboldt Wells, on the west boundary of Utah, and the Central Pacific rushing to reach Ogden, Utah, to give them an outlet to Salt Lake City.

In the building of a Pacific steam road to connect the two oceans two lines were graded alongside of each other for 225 miles between Ogden and Humboldt Wells. Climbing Promontory Mountain, they were not a stone's throw apart. When both companies saw that neither could reach its goal they came together and we made an agreement to join the tracks on the summit of Promontory Mountain, the Union Pacific selling to the Central Pacific fifty-six miles of its road back within five miles of Ogden and leasing trackage over that five miles to enable the Central Pacific to reach Ogden. These five miles were not only a part of the Union Pacific but used by their line north to Idaho. This agreement was ratified by Congress.

Each road built to the summit of Promontory, leaving a gap of about 100 feet of rail to be laid when the last spike was driven. The chief engineers of the Union and Central Pacific had charge of the ceremony and the work and we set a day far enough ahead so that trains coming from New York and San Francisco would have ample time to reach Promontory in time to take part in the ceremonies.

On the morning of May 10, 1869, Hon. Leland Stanford, Governor of California and President of the Central Pacific, accompanied by Messrs. Huntington, Hopkins, Crocker and trainloads of California's distinguished citizens, arrived from the west. During the forenoon Vice President T.C. Durant and Directors John B. Duff and Sidney Dillon and Consulting Engineer Silas A Seymour of the Union Pacific, with other prominent men including a delegation of Mormons from Salt Lake City, came in on a train from the east. The National Government was represented by a detachment of 'regulars' from Fort Douglas, Utah, accompanied by a band, and 600 others, including Chinese, Mexicans, Indians, half-breeds, negroes, and laborers, suggesting an air of cosmopolitanism all gathered around the open space where the tracks were to be joined. The Chinese laid the rails from the west end, and the Irish laborers laid them from the east end until they met and joined.

Telegraphic wires were so connected that each blow of the descending sledge could be reported instantly to all parts of the United States. Corresponding blows were struck on the

THE JUPITER (TRAIN) CARRIED LELAND STANFORD AND OTHER RAILWAY OFFICIALS TO GOLDEN SPIKE CEREMONY IN 1869

hill of the City Hall in San Francisco and with the last blow of the sledge a cannon was fired at Fort Point. General Safford presented a spike of gold, silver, and iron as the offering of the Territory of Arizona. Governor Tuttle of Nevada presented a spike of silver from his state. The connecting tie was of California laurel, and California presented the last spike of gold in behalf of that state. A silver sledge had also been represented for the occasion. A prayer was offered. Governor Stanford of California made a few appropriate remarks on behalf of the Central Pacific and the chief engineer responded for the Union Pacific. Then the telegraphic inquiry from the Omaha office, from which the circuit was to be started, was answered: "To everybody: Keep quiet. When the last spike is driven at Promontory Point we will say 'Done.' Don't break the circuit, but watch for the signals of the blows of the hammer. The spike will soon be driven. The signal will be three dots for the commencement of the blows."

The magnet tapped one-two-three-then paused—"Done." The spike was given its first blow by President Stanford and

GOLDEN SPIKE: "EAST AND WEST SHAKING HANDS AT THE LAYING OF LAST RAIL UNION PACIFIC RAILROAD—RESTORATION" BY ANDREW J. RUSSELL—YALE UNIVERSITY LIBRARIES

Vice President Durant followed. Neither hit the spike the first time, but hit the rail, and were greeted by the lusty cheers of the onlookers, accompanied by the screams of the locomotives and the music of the military band. Many other spikes were driven on the last rail by some of the distinguished persons present, but it was seldom that they first hit the spike. The original spike, after being tapped by the officials of the companies, was driven home by the chief engineers of the two roads. Then the two trains were run together, the two locomotives touch at the point of junction, and the engineers of the two locomotives each broke a bottle of champagne on the other's engine. Then it was declared that the connection was made and the Atlantic and Pacific were joined together never to be parted.

The wires in every direction were hot with congratulatory telegrams. President Grant and Vice President Colfax were the recipients of especially felicitous messages. On the evening of May 8th in San Francisco, from the stages of the theatres and other public places notice was given that the two roads had met and were to be wedded on the morrow. The celebration began at once and practically lasted through the 10th. The booming of cannons and the ringing of bells were united with other species of noise, making of which jubilant humanity finds expression for its feelings on such an occasion. The buildings in the city were gay with flags and bunting. Business was suspended and the longest processing that San Francisco had ever seen attested to the enthusiasm of the people. At night the city was brilliant with illuminations. Free railway trains filled Sacramento with an unwonted crowd, and the din of cannon, steam whistles and bells followed the final message.

At the eastern terminus in Omaha the firing of a hundred guns on Capitol hill, more bells and steam whistles and a grand processing of fire companies, civic societies, citizens and visiting delegations echoed the sentiments of the Californians. In Chicago a procession of four miles in length, a lavish display of decoration in the city and on the vessels in the river, and an address by Vice President Colfax in the evening were the evidences of the city's feeling. In New York, by order of the mayor, a salute of a hundred guns announced the culmination of the great undertaking. In Trinity Church the "to deum" was chanted, prayers were offered, and when the services were over the chimes rung out "Old Hundred," the "Ascension Carol" and national airs. The ringing of bells on Independence Hall and the fire stations in Philadelphia produced an unusual concourse of citizens to celebrate the national event. In the other large cities of the country the expressions of public gratification were hardly less hearty and demonstrative. Bret Harte was inspired to write the celebrated poem of "What the Engines Said." The first verse is: "What was it the engines said, Pilots touching, head to head, Facing on the single track, Half a world behind each back? This is what the engines said, Unreported and unread."[6]

6.   "How We Built the Union Pacific Railway and Other Railway Papers and Addresses." Major General Grenville M. Dodge, Chief Engineer Union Pacific Railway 1866–1870. 1908. Original text in the public domain. Retrieved from http://www.archive.org/stream/howwebuiltunionp00dodgrich/howwebuiltunionp00dodgr.

Clearly, this demonstrates the great excitement citizens everywhere felt. And yet today, few even think about the railroad trains as they pass by, except, perhaps, in an air of annoyance at the inconvenience of having to wait at a crossing. The union of the rails in 1869 changed history forever, joining two coasts and slowly starting the process of filling the land with people and enterprise on the great landscape that lay open between Nebraska and the Pacific.

A Good Deal for the Mormons?

The Union Pacific never did make full payment for the money it owed Brigham Young. He finally negotiated for surplus track and rolling stock to build a spur from Ogden to Salt Lake City, some thirty miles to the south (and his preferred route from the beginning). He was also granted a large block of shares in the Union Pacific that The Church of Jesus Christ of Latter-day Saints still owned well into the twentieth century. Harold B. Lee, President of the Church in the 1970s, was a respected member of the UP board of directors.

Two of Brigham Young's sons partnered with him in managing the railroad contracts and went on to build other trunk lines throughout Utah and Southeastern Idaho. Trains brought prosperity wherever the tracks reached.

Many of the laborers came up shorter in pay than they had agreed to simply because there was no money to pay them. But they still earned more than if they had been idle during that time. And the railroad did live up to its promise to bring more tourists. The number of visitors to Salt Lake City increased by more than a thousand times, and the isolation of the Saints decreased. Once again they were connected to the world, which accelerated their growth into the worldwide church of today.

As for the Union Pacific and the Central Pacific, their officers all agreed that the best work completed on the entire route was in those final stretches across the Utah desert and mountains. Brigham delivered fully on his end of the contracts, to the benefit of the entire country.

A Personal Connection

In 1975, fortune smiled, and I was given a job with the Union Pacific Railroad as a tracing clerk in the traffic department. My job was to find and track railroad cars for both the shippers and the receivers, using teletype messages to stations all across the UP line. Having loved railroads for as long as I could remember, this was really a great experience. I was perhaps a little too devoted to the cause when I took the history book *Union Pacific Country* on my honeymoon in July 1976.

In many ways, the railroads and telegraphs, which usually shared the same right of way, transformed the human world even more than the Internet has done in our generation. Prior to the railroads, the fastest a person had ever traveled on land was the speed of a racehorse. With the advent of trains, people could go more than 100 miles per hour on some stretches of the railroad, with few stops or breaks, even in the late 1860s. The way business was conducted changed forever. And it was the transcontinental railroad of the Union Pacific and Central Pacific that completed the physical linkage of the two coasts. I really liked being part of that heritage.

Ultimately I made a career as a financial advisor but never lost my love for the railroad. For example, I always visited the railroad museum in Sacramento when seeing my brother Dave, who lived there. We attended Rail Fair in 1976, commemorating the bicentennial of the country. It prominently featured the Freedom Train, a fully restored steam engine from the famous Daylight Series of the Southern Pacific, painted in patriotic red, white, and blue colors.

When our son Scott moved to Emeryville, California, in 2000, we decided to do something I've always wanted to do. Marcella and I traveled on Amtrak from Salt Lake City to Emeryville, which is the end of the line for the Union Pacific, on the shores of San Francisco Bay. For the first time, I had the chance to ride the route of the transcontinental railroad. We passed over the Bonneville Salt Flats, through the mountain deserts of Nevada to Reno, and then through the spectacular Sierra-Nevada Mountains near Tahoe. During the waning hours of sunlight, we passed through the fertile Sacramento Valley. It is a journey I recommend to everyone.

While this story focuses mostly on the Union Pacific, it was the builders of the Central Pacific through the Sierra-Nevada that holds the greatest drama. Chinese laborers wielding nitroglycerine and hammers carved out a path of tunnels, trusses, and ledges at enormous loss of human life. Snow tunnels had to be built to keep the railroad running in the winter, and even now the snow tunnels are still used. The switchbacks and grades required to climb to the top of the passes bear witness to the monumental achievement these nineteenth-century entrepreneurs completed, essentially creating modern America. It is a journey that is both beautiful and inspiring.

SOURCES

1. "The Pacific Railway Act." Primary Documents of American History (Virtual Services and Programs, Digital Reference Section, Library of Congress).

2. Full text of *How we built the Union Pacific railway, and ... (n.d.).* Retrieved from http://www.archive.org/stream/howwebuiltunionp00dodgrich/ howwebuiltunionp00dodgr with this additional information: Publisher [Council Bluffs, Ia. Monarch Printing Co. NOT_IN_COPYRIGHT Call number ucb_ banc:GLAD-84177415 Digitizing sponsor MSN Book contributor University of California Libraries. Collection cdl; americana.

3. *Nothing Like It in the World.* Stephen Ambrose. A Touchstone Book by Simon & Schuster, New York. 2000.

LEE DE FOREST WITH AUDION TUBE

CHAPTER 7

"INVISIBLE EMPIRE OF THE AIR"

Music and video are all around us—earbuds on the subway, televisions at the airport, spectacular surround-sound systems at the movie theaters. We take it for granted that we can easily hear a single voice amplified to fill a 100,000-seat football stadium or feel the heart-pounding throb of the bass guitar at a rock concert in an open-air amphitheater. Concerts, car sound systems, music videos—we love them all. Even more important, we are accustomed to having music, voice, and visual images transmitted through the air by radio, television, wireless Internet, and Bluetooth connections. We take our music and videos with us wherever we go because they are an integral part of our lives.

And yet, without Lee de Forest of Council Bluffs, Iowa, we might still be limited to hearing music and voice only as far as live musicians can project into the open air.

Simply stated, much of what makes the modern world modern can be attributed to the small cadre of inventors in the early twentieth century who labored to understand sound. They set out to capture, record, project, and transmit sound through wires and across the atmosphere via radio and microwaves. Because of them, virtually anyone, anywhere on the planet, can enjoy music and live action storytelling in a number of different ways. While it might appear to have been inevitable, a great deal of luck and serendipity brought about the electronic world we now take for granted.

THE AUDION

With more than 180 patents to his credit, Lee de Forest's principal innovation came early in his career. It was 1906 when he invented the audion, the first triode vacuum tube that made electronic amplification and detection possible.[1]

A triode is an electronic device capable of detecting the feeble, extremely high-frequency vibrations in the air that transmit radio, television, and mobile telephone signals, and then amplifying that pattern with electricity. Here's a simplified description of how it works:

1. The first element in the triode vacuum tube is the cathode, which is often called the filament. The filament is heated until it glows white hot. At this intense temperature of 2400 degrees Celsius, it starts to boil off negatively charged electrons. (F in the illustration*)

2. Because the second element in the triode, the anode (or plate) is physically cold, it carries a more positive charge than the cathode and thus attracts the surplus electrons. This means a current can flow in only one direction—from the cathode to the anode. (P in the illustration*)

3. De Forest's innovation was to insert a third element between the cathode and anode, which he called the grid. Rather than connect the radio antennae to the filament, as everyone had done before, de Forest connected the antennae to the grid so the grid vibrated in tune with the broadcast signal. (G in the illustration*)

4. As the surplus electrons pass through the grid in the vacuum, they take on the same wave pattern as the radio signal but are greatly amplified. The boiling electrons strike the anode in the same pattern as the radio wave.

---

1.   What makes the story even more interesting is that it was later shown that de Forest's initial explanation of how the audion works was flawed—he had invented a useable device without fully understanding the science behind it. His success was in recognizing how to apply his discovery.

5. The anode is attached to the output wire to decode this amplified signal to produce lower frequency audio waves the human ear can hear.

6. Once it reaches the correct frequency, the signal is amplified yet again using even more powerful triodes so it has enough energy to power the loudspeaker.

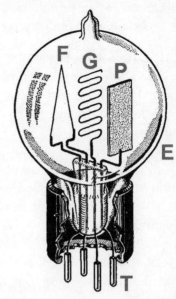

ILLUSTRATION BY K. E. THIEBAUD—RETRIEVED 17 OCTOBER 2013 FROM BASIC THEORY AND APPLICATION OF ELECTRON TUBES, US DEPT. OF THE ARMY TECHNICAL MANUAL TM 11-662, FEBRUARY

AUDION VACUUM TUBE CONSTRUCTION

While there are many steps in receiving and playing a radio broadcast (or television, telephone, radar, etc.), it all starts with de Forest's triode. The essential step is to amplify a small signal into a larger signal. His innovation was the key to instantaneous communication across vast distances, as well as to other important applications, as we shall see.

FROM LABORATORY TO REAL LIFE

In 1907, Lee used his invention to complete the first ship-to-shore broadcast from Lake Erie to his assistant, Frank Butler, on land. Frank clearly heard Lee's voice, even though Lee was miles away from the shore. It was a perceived miracle!

On January 12, 1910, Lee became the "Father of Public Radio" when he broadcast the *Tosca* from the Metropolitan Opera in New York City to the fortunate few with a radio receiver. Other shows followed the next day that featured Enrico Caruso, the famous opera singer. While many had heard Caruso's phonograph recordings, this was the first time they had heard his voice outside the concert hall, and this phenomenon was soon to change the world.

After proving the viability of radio in New York, de Forest moved to San Francisco where, in 1912, he began to create a design for a global radio network. Radio quickly attracted talented people and the financial resources needed to provide instantaneous voice communication in all areas of the economy (military, commercial, and personal conversations).

SERENDIPITY: SOUND AMPLIFICATION (KELLOGG AND RICE)

Once the triode was commercially available, it turned out to be a remarkably flexible invention that could detect all sorts of wave patterns, whether received through the air or from wires connected to other electronic devices.[2]

While de Forest spent his life working primarily in radio amplification, detecting high-frequency wave patterns invisible to humans, other inventors used the triode for a variety of purposes. The first was to provide sufficient amplification to increase the small electronic output of microphones and recording devices to drive loudspeakers. That was where C. W. Rice and E. W. Kellogg, inventors at the AT&T Laboratories in Schenectady, New York, entered the story. In 1921, they created the first practical electromechanical loudspeaker and patented it four years later.

Before Kellogg and Rice, sound amplification was accomplished mechanically using a horn. For example, Thomas Edison's phonograph in the late 1800s relied on recording voice and music through sound waves etched in wax discs. During playback, a stiff metal needle moved up and down in the wax while connected to a horn. Thus, the size of the horn limited the physical increase in volume.[3] While it was easy enough to fill a parlor, it was impossible to play recorded sound to an amphitheater.

The problem of sound amplification wasn't electronic. It was finding and organizing the materials needed to build a loudspeaker that could translate changes in electrical current into vibrations that mimicked the original sound.

It was to these problems that Rice and Kellogg turned their attention. They found the answer in the relationship between magnetic fields and copper coils. If they suspended a coil of wire in a magnetic field and

---

2.   In 1948, the transistor was invented using solid state elements instead of a vacuum tube, which dramatically reduced the energy consumption of the device; but the principle was still the same as de Forest's triode.

3.   The horn effect is easy to reproduce by cupping your hands and speaking or shouting in a specific direction—you sound louder to the people in the path of your focused sound.

physically moved the coil, it produced a current in the coil. In the reverse, if they applied an electric current to the coil inside the magnetic field, the coil would physically move up and down in response to the electronic signal. And thus, they had the mechanics of both a microphone and a loudspeaker. To create a microphone, they attached a small, cone-shaped diaphragm to a coil surrounded by a magnet. An electric current flowed when voice waves struck the diaphragm, which was then amplified by a triode in the same way as a radio transmitter. The increased electrical pattern was identical to the voice that created it.

The amplified electric signal from the amplifier, in turn, was fed to a much larger cone-shaped diaphragm attached to a larger wire coil used to make a loudspeaker. In this way, the small sound waves that struck the microphone were amplified in a very precise pattern to the much larger surface of the speaker, which could then project sound at high volumes.

Sound amplification could be done live, using a microphone connected directly to the amplifier and speakers, or it could come from a recorded source. Initially the movement of a stylus on the wax discs Thomas Edison invented used a crystal to create the electrical signal. Later, magnetic tape recorders and digital sources like cell phones and live Internet streaming would provide the signal. The key was converting the electrical signal into mechanical energy by use of the magnet and coil in the loudspeaker.

TRADITIONAL CONE LOUDSPEAKERS

Thus, Rice and Kellogg changed the world in 1925 with their development of high-fidelity microphones and speakers. The amount of amplification their discoveries made possible is remarkable. For example, an eighteen-inch powered subwoofer can generate more bass sound output than a thirty-foot, closed-end pipe organ! In fact, that's why many of the world's highest-quality concert organs have subwoofers to supplement the pipes to fill the concert hall with bone-rattling bass. And because of Rice and Kellogg, we can experience near-deafening volumes at rock concerts.[4]

But their success was only possible because of de Forest's invention of the triode, improved upon over the years but using the same fundamental principles.

A COMPLICATED LIFE

Not all of Lee de Forest's inventions were successful, and they were costly to pursue, not to mention he was highly litigious in fighting for his patents.

But he was a real genius. Perhaps his second most notable invention was the system he developed to record sound on motion picture film. Having identified an anode material sensitive to light, he started recording voice and music as varying gray strips that ran parallel to the moving photos on the reel. This method synchronized sound to the dialog. His system replaced an earlier attempt to coordinate a vinyl record with the images on the screen, which suffered from the defect that the voice and movements were often out of sync. Without the creative mind of Lee de

---

4.   It wasn't long before loudspeakers were in frequent use in radios and movie theatres. Manufacturers learned that small cones are best for reproducing high-frequency sounds (tweeters) and large cones, up to thirty inches in circumference with great movement within the magnetic field, are best for producing deep bass notes (woofers). Most speakers have a midsized speaker to cover the midrange. There are other variations to loudspeaker designs, such as electrostatic, the Heil air motion transformer, and others, but they all use the same process of moving a mass in response to the electric circuit. The basic electromechanical loudspeaker Kellogg and Rice invented remains the most economical way to produce high-quality sound, even today. By the way, some loudspeaker manufacturers, such as Klipschorn, still put a horn in front of the electromechanical loudspeaker to gain astonishing outputs of volume relative to the electrical input. Old is still new.

Forest, the lavish musical score in *Gone with the Wind* and *The Wizard of Oz* and all the movies since wouldn't have worked nearly as well.

UNIVERSITY OF UTAH—DR. THOMAS STOCKHAM AND THE DIGITAL INNOVATION

It's a testament to Thomas Edison's creativity that vinyl records survived as the primary recording medium for high-fidelity music for nearly 100 years. Magnetic tape recording became an alternative, but it had a distracting background hissing noise. As for vinyl records, they could easily be scratched, which meant that when the stiff needle crossed a damaged groove, there was a popping and crackling sound. In both media, the quality of the recorded sound deteriorated with each playback.

Dr. Thomas Stockham, a professor at the University of Utah, created a solution to this problem in the early 1970s. He was the first to figure out how to digitize the sine wave pattern of a sound wave so it could be read and repeated by a computer. Once this process was mastered, the sound was recorded using a laser beam that etched a hard plastic compact disc, or CD. Light replaced the mechanical process of the needle or tape head and, in doing so, eliminated much of the distortion in recordings.

What does digital mean? The long sine wave pattern of audible sound is broken up into thousands of pulses that are either on or off. These pulses form a pattern that accurately produces the original wave by increasing or decreasing the amplitude of each pulse. It may sound technical, but in a way, it is just a variation of how radio decodes very high-frequency waves into the lower-frequency sound waves that are discernible to the human ear. Stockham's genius was to move recording and decoding to computers that quickly read the digital impulses.

One consequence of his invention is the reduction of space needed to store music and voice. A 5,000-song vinyl-record collection weighs approximately 150 pounds. That same music weighs fifteen pounds on compact discs. Today, the same library requires just a few ounces of solid-state media on your iPhone. People can now travel with their entire music collection. Best of all, they never hear scratches or hisses because the computer can sort out any unwanted variations in the sound pattern and eliminate them.

DINNER WITH AMAR G. BOSE

In 1968, my world changed when I heard Bose 901 loudspeakers for the first time. My father loved music, having played jazz trumpet when he was young, so our house was frequently filled with music from his Magnavox console stereo. I thought that was all there was to sound. But then one of my best friends, Paul Cleaver, purchased a set of Bose 901.

We were only in the ninth grade, and Bose cost a small fortune, but Paul wanted the best. Somehow he had heard of these remarkable new speakers and had saved the money to buy them. Inviting me into the sound room in his basement, he played the new hit song "If You're Going to San Francisco." The sound was astonishing, surrounding us with crystal-clear treble and deep, powerful bass. It seemed to engulf us. I'd never heard anything like it in my life, and I'm sure my jaw dropped as I asked Paul to play it over and over again.

These new Bose speakers were unlike any other loudspeaker on the market. All other brands aimed their speakers straight forward. To get the correct stereo sound, you had to position your chair precisely in the middle of the room, equal distance between the two speakers. But Bose created a very different sound field by aiming eight out of nine speakers on angled panels on the back of the speaker cabinet. This meant the sound reflected off the back and side walls of the room before reaching the listener. It was as if the sound was coming from everywhere, and it hooked me the first time I heard it.

The first lesson I learned in the world of high-quality audio was the difference between the mediocre single-cabinet sound I'd grown up with and true audiophile speakers. The best speakers at that time included Acoustic Research, JBL, Altec-Lansing, ESS, KLH, and Klipsch. Paul and I spent hundreds of hours during our high school years listening to speakers, including acoustic suspension, bass reflex, horn-loaded, and electrostatic speakers. We tried to discern the subtlest differences in their sound as we searched for the perfect speaker. The Bose 901 wasn't perfect, but it re-created the sound field in a way no one had previously imagined possible, and that is what made it revolutionary. Its high-frequency sound came closest to the industry standard electrostatic speaker while using a traditional cone speaker at a far lower cost and with much better bass. It was this ideal combination of sound and price that was so compelling to my friends and me. The history of its development is interesting.

Dr. Amar G. Bose was a professor of acoustical engineering at the Massachusetts Institute of Technology (MIT). He was also an avid fan of live-orchestra classical music. Even though he purchased the finest audio speakers on the market, the sound of his home stereo never came close to the sound he heard in the concert hall. So he set out to investigate why. What he discovered was that the audio standards of the time judged speakers on their ability to reproduce accurate tones. Speakers were tested in an anechoic chamber (a room with no parallel surfaces to create standing waves) with a microphone positioned directly between the two stereo speakers. The goal was to measure the sound with no reverberations. Using this method, whichever company came closest to reproducing the sine-wave pattern of the input signal was

DR. AMAR G. BOSE WITH A BOSE 901; NOTICE 8 SPEAKERS ON THE BACK SIDE TO REFLECT AGAINST THE WALLS, AND 1 SPEAKER, NOT SHOWN, FACING FORWARD

judged to be the best speaker. It also required a listener to position himself very carefully in the environment. User manuals of the time suggested that to get the real stereophonic sound, the listener had to sit directly at the apex of a triangle between the two speakers. Anyone sitting on either side of this ideal spot heard one side more loudly than the other.

But Bose's extensive studies in live concert halls showed that only 11 percent of sound reached a person in the audience directly. The other 89 percent first reflects off other surfaces, including the ceiling, instruments, walls, and floor. In this live environment, we sense the size of the room from the way these direct and delayed sound waves strike our ear, and it's from this multitude of signals that we discern the music. But in the home and, even worse, in an anechoic chamber, all these pleasant reverberations are lost, and the music feels cumbersome and lifeless. At least that's how it sounded to Amar Bose.

The Bose 901 was small in comparison to loudspeakers of the time, relying on nine four-and-a-half-inch drivers with long-throw cones and a lot of input power to create the sound needed to fill a room. And with the angled speakers and reflection in the room, it sounded like a concert hall and a live performance![5]

While most young men of high school age save their money for cars, my friends and I saved our money to buy stereo equipment. It became an obsession. Eventually I went to work as a salesman for Clark Partridge of Clark's Audio, selling high-end audio equipment. And this was how I came to meet Dr. Bose.

As Paul and I became more experienced in sound, we happened to attend a school dance where they were playing the music through a thirty-year-old overhead sound system. It was awful. No one cared to dance because they could hardly hear the music, let alone feel it. But the school couldn't afford a live band, so that was it. As we talked about it later, we figured we could do sound a lot better than that, so we volunteered to play recorded music for our upcoming junior assembly. We hooked our Bose 901 to Paul's powerful state-of-the-art SAE amplifier and played the most popular music of 1970 as a warm up. No one had ever before heard anything like it, and it was a spectacular success. So much so that Paul and I were hired to do school dances all across Southeastern Idaho for the balance of our high school years.

The unintended consequence of this first auditorium experience was that we started plugging microphones into our system to amplify people talking. When Paul and I placed our 901s at the front edge of the stage, with the back side facing out into the auditorium, the spoken word became crystal clear in virtually every seat in the hall, much different from the unintelligible garble students had listened to for decades. In such a large room, we didn't need to reflect the sound first; the hall itself did that. With their high-fidelity sound positioned right in front of the performers, the Bose made both voice and music astonishingly clear. At the end of the performance, people mobbed us to know how we did it. Fortuitously this included

5.   Today, front-facing speakers achieve wide sound dispersion by using tweeters with a 180-degree sound field. Some use an inverted cone. This gives the open effect Dr. Bose pioneered but in a more traditional configuration. Surround sound also re-creates the ambiance of live environments by using multiple speakers positioned both in front of and behind the listener. Intentional delays are created electronically to create the effect of various settings, including large concert halls, small clubs, etc.

our high school principal! For one of the first times in his tenure, people had paid attention because they could hear and understand what was going on. So he rented Paul and me for all school assemblies for the next two years. The fee from meetings and dances helped us buy even more equipment.

As our time in school was nearing its end, the principal requested funds from the school district to buy a new sound system. The school district's purchasing committee hired a consultant out of Salt Lake City to draft specifications for this new system. Because the consultant came at the task from a traditional point of view, the new system called for specifications only new Voice of the Theatre speakers with new electronics could meet. So devious was the consultant in drafting his specifications that only one vendor in the Intermountain West could meet the specs—the company he represented.

Paul and I were outraged that new technology hadn't been considered.[6] We had helped Clark Partridge, who owned a local audio store, submit a bid for a modern Bose system, which we had proved worked so well, but our competitor said we were trying to fit a home stereo into an auditorium-sized space, making us look like amateurs. Of course, that added to our indignation.

In spite of our protests, it looked like he was going to win. We were discouraged, but Clark was somehow calm. It turned out he had an ace in the hole. Because Clark was the factory representative for Bose Corporation in the Intermountain West, as well as an early advocate for Bose, he made a call to Massachusetts, and that set up the drama for the upcoming school board meeting.[7]

When the new sound system came up for approval on the agenda, we requested permission to speak. I said a few words about our experiences over the past two years. Then Clark, as submitter of one of the rejected bids, stepped forward to explain why the consultant's specifications were flawed and why the school board should discard them as they chose a new system. This provoked consternation from the board members, with

---

6.   It takes passion and idealism to achieve outrage over something like a sound system. But then, youth are famous for both.

7.   In fact, Clark Partridge had been friends with Dr. Bose for many years and was one of the first distributors in the country to agree to sell his speakers when the company was first founded. He even owned a pair of prototype 901s, with serial numbers minus four and minus three.

one of them saying, "How can I make a judgment like that. How can we challenge the conclusions of an audio expert?"

"An audio expert?" Clark asked innocently. "If we could provide a world-recognized authority on sound reproduction, would you be willing to listen to him?" The board mumbled that they would. At which point, Clark said with a flourish, "Then perhaps you'll allow me to introduce Dr. Amar G. Bose of the Massachusetts Institute of Technology!" There was an audible gasp, particularly since many in the room were Clark's customers and owned a set of the revolutionary new Bose speakers themselves.

Dr. Bose stepped out of the shadows and came to the microphone, where he wowed the audience with his charm, grace, and knowledge. A man with a slight build, he commanded attention through the sheer intelligence of what he had to say. First he established the scientific principles that allowed the school board to scrap the original bid. And then he surprised even us by saying that while he thought our proposal was reasonable, he believed we could install a system for only half the price by making a few minor modifications in the electronics. The board swooned and asked him to help us submit the new bid. They would save money, and the school would get a new state-of-the-art sound system. We were ecstatic.

Exiting the meeting in triumph, we adjourned to the Hong Kong Cuisine, where we had the chance to have a private dinner with my audio hero. During dinner, Dr. Bose questioned Paul and me extensively on how we used our system for school dances and voice reproduction. I proudly told him about an exchange trip we took with others in our class to an Idaho Falls area high school where we used our speakers as students were entering the auditorium. Some of the students had come up to ask us where the live band was—our recorded music sounded that good. Bose nodded his head, said he'd pondered if there was a place for Bose in the commercial world, and then told us he appreciated our insights. It was a few months later that we installed the new sound system in the Pocatello High School auditorium, the first in the world for a Bose large-room application.

Today, of course, Bose is everywhere. I listen with Bose noise-canceling earbuds when traveling and have Bose computer speakers plugged into my office computer. And Bose has a large share of the home surround-sound market now. They also have some terrific commercial installations all around the world, with a particularly sweet spot in small clubs and dance halls. I'm sure they'd have gotten there eventually without us, but the fact that we played a part in opening a new market for this remarkable company is gratifying.

I recently read many of the tributes to Amar Bose when he passed away. His students loved him (he continued teaching at MIT, even after Bose Corporation became a worldwide enterprise), and the audio world celebrated his contribution to both sound reproduction and the live theater. I remember him as the charmingly self-effacing man who told us over dinner that the milkshakes we had at the Hong Kong Cuisine that night were called frappes in his native Boston. It was at that young age that I learned that great inventors are often modest but driven men.

IT'S ALL ABOUT THE MUSIC

Lee de Forest once said, "I have discovered an invisible empire of the air, intangible, yet solid as granite."[8] Indeed he had. The jump of electrons between anodes and cathodes, the invisible magnetic fields between speaker coil and magnet, and the millions of high-frequency and ultra-high-frequency waves that reverberate through the air make our modern world possible. Smartphones, wireless data streams, and high-definition video were always available to man, but it took the best instincts, combined with trial and error of great minds like de Forest, Kellogg, Rice, Stockham, and thousands more to turn them into inventions that enrich our daily lives.

Perhaps even more intriguing is wondering what comes next and discovering who the inventors are who will successfully alter the future in ways not yet imagined.

SOURCES

1. Lee de Forest, King of Radio, Television, and Film. Mike Adams. 2012 Copernicus Books, an Imprint of Springer Science+Business Media. New York.

2. "Lee de Forest." Wikipedia, the Free Encyclopedia. Wikimedia Foundation, Inc. 28 April 2015. 1 May 2015. http://en.wikipedia.org/wiki/Lee_de_Forest.

3. History and Types of Loudspeakers. Edison Tech Center. 2015. The Edison Tech Center a 501(c)(3) nonprofit. New York. http://edisontechcenter.org/speakers.html.

___

8.   *Sounds and Images. Media and Culture: An Introduction to Mass Communication.* Richard Campbell, Christopher R. Martin, and Bettina Fabos. Boston: Bedford/St. Martin's. 2000. 113, and additional text.

4. "Thomas Stockham." Wikipedia, the Free Encyclopedia. Wikimedia Foundation, Inc. 25 February 2015. 1 May 2015. http://en.wikipedia.org/wiki/Thomas_Stockham.

GLEN CANYON DAM NEAR PAGE ARIZONA, JUST NORTH OF THE GRAND CANYON; NOTE
THAT ALL WATER RELEASE GATES ARE OPEN, AND WATER IS ARCING OUT AT THE BASE OF THE
DAM FROM OVERFLOW TUNNELS ON BOTH SIDES OF THE CANYON

CHAPTER 8

HOW FOUR FEET OF PLYWOOD SAVED THE GRAND CANYON

"The really scary story is when we nearly lost the Glen Canyon Dam in 1983."

"Lost the Glen Canyon Dam? What are you talking about?"

By way of background, Glen Canyon Dam is a fifty-story concrete-arch dam that creates Lake Powell, the second largest reservoir in North America by volume. It seemed impossible that this dam, just north of the Grand Canyon, nearly failed.

"It was a very close call," my friend, a dam inspector with the U.S. Bureau of Reclamation, said. "We were literally down to the last few inches before the lake overtopped the emergency spillway without any way to stop it. We'd opened every gate and tunnel, and red water from the overflow basin gushed out at the base of the dam. It looked to me as if the dam was bleeding."[1]

Now, that is a visual image not to be forgotten: red sandstone saturating the water arcing out in a fantastic torrent from the base of one of the largest dams in the world. Red water meant the concrete lining of the tunnels had failed, and erosion was eating away at the sandstone walls that buttressed the dam. Had this erosion reached the reservoir, Lake Powell would have drained, sending a 500-foot-high wave of water down the narrow canyons of the Colorado, directly into the

---

1. Original interview with a retired dam inspector. 2015. Name withheld by request.

Grand Canyon. There it would have wreaked havoc on one of the seven wonders of the natural world.

Not only that, but once it had smashed through the Grand Canyon, it would have plowed right into Lake Mead behind Hoover Dam, which was already at full capacity. With nowhere else to go but over the top of Hoover Dam, it would have destroyed the powerhouse at the base of that dam and continued to create a domino effect of failing dams all the way downstream to Mexico.[2]

Visualizing this wave of destruction was an image I simply couldn't shake.

A Brief History of the Colorado River Dams

Hoover Dam, completed in 1935, was the first attempt in human history to contain a river with the force and flow of the Colorado. Prior to Hoover Dam, the Colorado had caused massive flooding in Southern California and Arizona. In fact, in 1904, the head gates of an irrigation canal from the lower Colorado into the Imperial Basin, near Palm Springs, had been washed out by floods. The unrestricted flow of the Colorado had started to fill the ancient below-sea-level sink with water and, in the process, had created what is today known as the Salton Sea. It took heroic efforts to close the breach at the head of this canal to restore the Colorado to its historic channel. With the canal destroyed, hundreds of profitable farms were put out of business. This disaster proved that the water flows from the Colorado were far too uncertain for agricultural use unless managed by a dam. But it would have to be a monumental dam to handle even the most massive of floods.

In the absence of such a dam, agricultural production in Southern California came to a halt. In 1932, construction was started on Hoover Dam, which was built to the highest engineering standards, a modern pyramid that rises more than seventy stories from the foundation to the crest. It now impounds Lake Mead, the largest reservoir in North America based on volume. Once the dam was complete, the new "All American Canal" was built from Yuma, Arizona, to the Imperial Valley to water more than four million acres of California agriculture with

---

2.   Hoover Dam is made of concrete that would have likely survived the overtopping. But many of the dams south of Hoover Dam are earth filled, and an overtopped earth-fill dam is almost certain to fail.

GLEN CANYON DAM FROM DOWNSTREAM ON THE EASTERN BANK OF THE COLORADO RIVER

steady, controlled flows. The river also provided municipal water to both Los Angeles and Phoenix and other southwestern cities. Presently, more than 30 million people depend on the Colorado for water and agriculture. Hoover Dam also generates enormous amounts of electricity, and the federal government has used this source of revenue to fully repay the cost of building and operating the dam. Today it is a moneymaker for the U.S. government.

Once Hoover was completed, the Bureau of Reclamation went on a dam-building spree. For example, Hoover Dam was the first in the world to rise higher than five stories. Since then, more than 45,000 dams have been built as high or greater.[3] Included in that total is the massive Glen Canyon Dam and Lake Powell, built in the arid and sweltering region of the high-mountain desert of Utah and Arizona.

Glen Canyon Dam came into being when the success at Hoover made it appear that the river could easily support a second large dam. Pressure started building to add to the total storage capacity by building a new dam near Page, Arizona. Congress authorized the gigantic concrete

3.   River of Surprise. 6.

115

LAKE POWELL FROM NORTH OF THE GLEN CANYON DAM

arch dam in 1955, in spite of strident controversy from environmentalists and preservationists who did not want to lose ancient Native American writings and artifacts in the area.

Construction started in 1956, and the Glen Canyon Dam was completed September 13, 1963. It took seventeen years for the reservoir to fill to capacity, and as water backed behind the dam, it slowly flooded the many side canyons that reach like fingers back into the sandstone flats. To give an idea of how complicated the topography is at Lake Powell, consider that the lake backs up 186 miles, but the shoreline is more than 1,960 miles because of the many side canyons and coves. It is an artificial wonder created on top of the great natural wonder of the former Glen Canyon.

The primary purpose of the Glen Canyon Dam was water storage, as evidenced by the title of the enabling legislation, "The Colorado River Storage Project." With water storage as the primary objective, the goal was to store additional water at Glen Canyon in high-water years so it could be released in low-water years to replenish Lake Mead.

Generating electricity was listed as a second objective, which outraged 1950s environmentalists who thought that inundating Glen Canyon was a horrible price to pay for electricity. Most famous among the protesters was Edward Abbey, who wrote the best-selling book *The Monkey Wrench Gang*, which talked about all the ways he and other radical environmentalists hoped to stop the dam before it was built. Once they saw that construction of the dam was inevitable, they plotted how to destroy it before the lake filled. But Abbey's fantasies remained unfulfilled, and Lake Powell climbed its way to maximum depth in 1980. This first filling of the reservoir was intentional. The next time it occurred, in 1983, it was not.

Another objective for the dam was recreation. Lake Powell became a terrific venue for more than 3 million visitors each year.

And finally, because of the heavy silt load the Colorado River carries, Lake Powell now receives an estimated 45 million tons of sediment at the upper reaches of the pool, a new diversion of the residue that protects Lake Mead, which has extended the useful life of Hoover Dam by many hundreds of years.[4] Taking into consideration all these benefits, combined with the political forces in favor of building the dam, it made sense to move the project forward.

There were challenges that came with the Glen Canyon Dam:

- The primary problem is related to the soft and unstable Navajo sandstone the dam's canyon walls and floor abut. *Desert USA* characterizes it as "solidified sand dunes."[5] In contrast, Hoover Dam, built in Black Canyon more than 400 miles to the south, is built on a foundation of extremely hard andesite breccias— not easily eroded. This was a significant difference when the overflow tunnels were flooded at both dams in the high-water years of 1983 and 1984.

- Current thinking also suggests that the sediment load being deposited into Lake Powell should be handled differently. As it is now, the entire natural environment of the river has changed from being a carrier of a large silt load the full length of the river to one discharging crystal-clear, cold water at the base of each of the dams. Naturally this impacts the ecology of the river and the various aquatic creatures and plants that have adapted to the

---

4.   Of course, this also means that the storage capacity of Lake Powell diminishes by the amount of siltation on an annual basis.

5.   *Desert USA.* http://www.desertusa.com/gc/gcd/du_glencaydam.html. September 26, 2015.

GLEN CANYON DAM WESTERN OVERFLOW TUNNEL INLET AS SEEN FROM LAKE POWELL; NOTE THE SOFT CHARACTER OF SANDSTONE

historical pattern over many thousands of years. If either of these dams were to be built today, the engineers would create a sediment canal and tunnel to bring silt around the reservoir to be redeposited into the river at the base of the dam. This would solve the siltation problems at both Lake Powell and Lake Mead, as well as keeping the river below the dams in a more natural state.

• There is also a problem of evaporation in low-water years. While it makes great sense to double the water storage of the river in high-water years, having water dispersed over two lakes in low-water years means twice as much evaporative surface. According to Daniel P. Beard, a former commissioner of the Bureau of Reclamation, this evaporative loss at Lake Powell averages 860,000 acre-feet of water annually.[6] He indicates this "is enough water to meet the yearly water requirements of the city of Los Angeles in 2015. In fact," he says, "Lake Powell loses more than six percent of the Colorado River's annual flow through evaporation and

---

6.   An acre-foot of water is 326,000 gallons, which is enough to cover an acre in one foot of water. Or it would fill an Olympic-size swimming pool halfway.

bank seepage."[7] While 1983 enjoyed spectacular rainfalls, the decades following have seen record droughts, which means that far less water would be lost if the full flow of the Colorado made its way to Lake Mead.[8]

With all that said, however, the Glen Canyon Dam *was* built, and Lake Powell *does* exist. And in 1983, the Bureau of Reclamation discovered, to its horror, that design flaws in the emergency overflow tunnels threatened the viability of the dam. They had to act quickly to minimize the disaster and to mitigate the risks in future years.

RECORD RAINFALLS—1982 THROUGH 1984

After the dam filled to capacity in 1980, the water managers at Lake Powell kept the reservoir at capacity since that assured the highest possible water volume for electricity generation. When rainfall in late 1982 and early 1983 came in at record levels (210 percent above average), they should have drawn down both Lake Powell and Lake Mead as rapidly as possible. But according to engineers at the dam, the *predicted* water flow into Lake Powell stayed at around 100 percent right up until the first of June. So until *actual* water-flow statistics were available, there appeared to be no urgency to let water out. It was only in late spring that they realized their mistake and immediately took emergency action.

First they opened seven of the eight penstock gates. These gates control water flow into the steel-lined tubes that spin the power turbines at the base of the dam. One turbine was offline for maintenance, so that gate was unavailable.[9] Next they opened the four outlet gates close to the base of the dam that send water directly into the river without passing

---

7.   *Deadbeat Dams*. Daniel P. Beard. Johnson Books, a Big Earth Publishing company. Colorado. 2015. 72–73.

8.   Dan Beard was appointed commissioner by Interior Secretary Bruce Babbit, a strong environmentalist. Beard is a fierce opponent of nearly all dams. He was forced to resign from his post at USBR after embarrassing the United States when, as an official guest in China, he derided the Three Gorges Dam and declared it a mistake.

9.   Live interview with Richard Fehr, Duane Berrier, and Chris Mauger at Glen Canyon Dam on August 28, 2015. Richard and Chris are engineers with the U.S. Bureau of Reclamation. Duane worked at the dam in 1983 and now serves as a tour guide.

Lake Powell aerial photo in 1983; the water level has been artificially raised above design "full pool" because of record rainfall; note water exiting the overflow tunnels downstream from the base of the dam

through the turbines. It is the output of these four gates that creates the most sense of drama since the water comes arcing out under incredible pressure.

But within days, it was apparent that these traditional steps weren't enough to counter the flow into the lake, even with all the gates wide open. The reservoir level continued to climb. By June, it reached the base of the emergency overflow gates that were designed to send excess water into massive tunnels carved out of the soft Navajo sandstone and then lined with concrete.

To give a sense of how much water the Colorado was carrying in 1983, the overflow tunnels at Glen Canyon and Hoover Dam were designed to release as much water as typically flows over Niagara Falls on an average day. Before the crisis ended, tunnels at both dams were beyond maximum capacity! Another way of visualizing the volume of water is to note that the overflow basins at the top of each of the tunnels at Hoover are large enough to float a World War II aircraft carrier.

So what was the problem? These tunnels had been designed specifically for a situation like this. Just as planned, when the overflow gates were opened, water poured into the overflow basin and then entered the three-story-high tunnels. Gravity pulled the water down the tunnels to allow it to exit into the river far downstream of the dam. But there was a problem in the tunnels. Reporter Philip L. Fradkin described the trouble at the Glen Canyon Dam in a 1995 article in the *Los Angeles Times*:

> Two thousand tons of water per second soared from the dam's two spillways and river outlets. Rumbling noises started in early June. Chunks of rocks and pieces of concrete issued from the spillway tunnels as if the dam was mortally wounded. Despite the apparent damage, the spillway gates needed to be kept partially open because the reservoir was rising almost six inches a day. Yet water also needed to be contained. Hoover Dam, 402 miles downstream, had safety problems of its own, and releases from Hoover could cause extensive flooding and damage all the way to the Gulf of California, as it eventually did that year. Top bureau officials met in late June and established a maximum water level of 3,708 feet above sea level for Lake Powell. At 3,708.40 feet, the engineers thought they would lose control of the spillway gates. Four-foot-high plywood sheets were added as flashboards to the gates. The water rose and lapped over them. The plywood was replaced by eight-foot steel plates. The water still rose. When engineers inspected the spillway tunnels, they saw that house-sized holes had been punched through the concrete lining and into the sandstone. They thought the sandstone might erode, causing an uncontrolled release, according to a memo. . . . The level of the reservoir peaked at 3,708.34 feet on July 15, *six-hundredths of a foot below the point where officials feared they'd lose control*. It held steady for a few days and then gradually declined."[10]

How could these planned overflow tunnels fail?

- As Lake Powell's water level rose to the level of the overflow gates, officials released water into the tunnels as planned. But in all their calculations of the potential flow of the river, the designers of the dam had never anticipated that the tunnels would fill all the way

---

10. "The Year the Dam (Almost) Broke." Philip L. Fradkin. October 29, 1995. *The Los Angeles Times*. http://articles.latimes.com/1995-10-29/magazine/tm-62672_1_hoover-dam. 06/19/2015. Emphasis added.

to the top. Rather, they expected there would be headroom in the tubes to handle air bubbles trapped in the cascading water.

- In 1983, the tunnels filled to the top as the water started its steep descent from the crest of the dam down seventy stories to the base of the dam at the river. Imagine a steeply sloped tunnel that, near the base of the dam, connected to an original

Erosion in an overflow tunnel; note the concrete lining at the top; the lining is stripped away at the bottom, allowing erosion of the sandstone wall

122

diversion tunnel used during construction of the dam to divert river water around the dam site. This original tunnel had a very shallow slope. The compression of the water at this elbow junction was tremendous.

• As this highly pressurized water encountered the textured surface of the concrete lining, it flowed at different velocities than the water moving away from the lining. This differential created a vacuum in a phenomenon called "cavitation." The incredible flow of 1983 was enough for this cavitation to suck the concrete lining away from the sandstone rock of the tunnels. Then the sandstone immediately started being torn away in large chunks that caused the massive dam itself to shudder as these chunks passed down the overflow tunnels.

• The problem was most severe at the juncture where the steeply sloped tunnel met the original diversion tunnel, since both the direction of the flow and the pressure of the water changed at that point. This abrupt change in flow increased the destructive effect of the cavitation and tore the concrete lining to pieces.

The engineers' fear was that this erosion would eventually claw its way back toward both the base and the sides of the dam. If the tunnels eroded to the lake itself, the dam would become useless, as the water in the reservoir would just flow around it via the compromised tunnels into the river below. If this process began, it would accelerate quickly into a full failure.

As it was, the noise from failing concrete and sandstone being hurled down the overflow tunnels and then ejected out into the river was so loud people four miles away heard it. The dam itself vibrated and shuddered, and as my friend indicated at the beginning of this chapter, the flow of red, silt-saturated water from the base of the dam was ominous. It was later discovered that erosion in the left tunnel had dislodged a boulder nearly the size of a house and it was trapped inside the tunnel, bouncing up and down like a marble in a tube. It was this boulder crashing against the ceiling and floor that caused the entire dam to shudder. It thudded every two seconds, as if connected to a metronome.[11]

---

11. Live interview with U.S. Bureau of Reclamation engineers at Glen Canyon Dam. August 28, 2015.

On June 19, so much material was torn loose inside the tunnel that one jet at the base of the dam plugged up. For the engineers, the only choice at that point was to open the overflow gates 100 percent to put extra pressure inside the tunnel to blow this obstruction free. They did that, and it worked. People at the site were amazed as they watched huge chunks of concrete, some the size of automobiles, shooting out more than eighty feet from the base of the dam. They had solved the immediate problem but only by making the erosion in the tunnels even worse.

SAVING THE DAM

Fortunately the Glen Canyon Dam did not fail, and Lake Powell is still doing what it was originally designed to do. The engineers averted failure because of some very innovative thinking and some heroic actions at that time. The men and women who responded to the crisis made incredible exertions to save the dam, as well as the landscape and the communities below it.

To better understand what was happening and to assess the situation before the lake reached full capacity, engineers closed the overflow gate on the left tunnel and entered the tunnel from the top to see what was going on inside. It was during this inspection that they discovered the cavitation at the tunnel elbow was so extreme that it had carved out a cavern larger than a full-size house. Obviously the cavitation was far more serious and had done much more damage than they had anticipated.

They concluded that the danger from this erosion was greater on the right tunnel (facing downstream) since it passed closer to the footings of the dam, so their priority was to maximize use of the left tube as much as possible to protect the right tube.

Once they were clear on what was happening in the tunnels, they realized the greatest danger to the dam was uncontrolled flow into the tubes if the reservoir topped the overflow gates. In contemplating potential solutions, a group of engineers onsite in Page, Arizona, met to confer. In this meeting, USBR engineer Richard Fehr thought about a pile of plywood sheets in the powerhouse. He said, "We had been in discussions about how we could raise the level of the lake. What was needed was to add capacity at the top of the radial gates on each side of the reservoir. It struck me that this plywood could do the job. After all, four feet of water is just one and three-fourths pounds per square inch."

Plywood may sound like a flimsy solution to holding back an entire reservoir, but it was similar to sandbagging along a river. The force of four feet of water at the top of the lake was no more than four feet of water in a backyard swimming pool, which could be contained in a thin plastic lining. Pressure only increased with depth. Richard went on to say, "We were sitting around a table in Page, Arizona, talking with our Denver headquarters when I proposed this. At first they said it sounded crazy, but when I asked them to do the math, they calculated that it might work. So we sketched out a quick design for some triangular-shaped brackets that could be welded to the top of the radial gates in a way

PLYWOOD SHEETS ADDED TO THE TOP OF THE RADIAL OVERFLOW GATE ON EACH SIDE OF THE RESERVOIR; THIS SIMPLE ADDITION TO THE GATES ALLOWED THE RESERVOIR TO RISE AN ADDITIONAL FOUR FEET, WHICH PROVIDED TIME TO CONTROL WATER GOING INTO THE DAMAGED OVERFLOW TUNNELS

that bolstered the plywood. Denver gave their approval, and I took it down to the fabrication shop. We had sixteen people working onsite, so I assigned eight people to go home and rest while the other eight started fabrications. When I came back later that evening, the fabrication was done. So the eight of us who were rested strung wire across the top of the gate so we could go out on the slick surface and start welding the uprights."[12]

At this point, it was raining, which made the task even more dangerous and particularly frightening, since the grate across the top of the gate on which they were standing was only eighteen inches wide! Richard said, "It was downright scary because it was dark and water was cascading out into the overflow basin from the base of the radial gates we were working on. The noise was incredible, with mist coming up from the overflow basin and rain falling from above. We installed the flashboards on the left (east) spillway gates the same night the brackets were fabricated. The work in the dark in the rain on top of those spillway grates was a most terrifying job, yet it was done without complaint by the crews, who were true heroes to put themselves at risk like that. The flashboards on the right spillway gates were installed the next day. We had safety lines attached, but who wanted to be suspended by a safety line above the torrent of water raging just a few feet below us? But we stayed at it until the new plywood barriers were in place, and then we went home exhausted."[13]

To their relief, this very simple, straightforward solution reduced the flow into the tunnels, as planned.

With this additional four feet of storage at the top of the gates, the engineers gained enough time to control the amount of water flowing into the overflow basins. But as the reservoir climbed to the brim of this four-foot extension, they replaced the plywood with eight-foot steel sheets to allow the reservoir to rise even farther.

When the water got to within .004 inches of the top of the eight-foot metal sheets, there was nothing more they could do. The extensions had raised the reservoir to within a few feet of the top of the dam itself. To add any additional height to the temporary bulwarks would overtop the dam, allowing water to pour down over the front of the dam itself.

---

12. Ibid.
13. Ibid.

HASTILY FABRICATED 8-FOOT STEEL BARRICADES REPLACE THE PLYWOOD SHEETS TO ALLOW THE RESERVOIR TO RISE TO ITS MAXIMUM POSSIBLE DEPTH; THIS CREATED A NEW PROBLEM—THE MACHINERY THAT CONTROLLED THE GATES HAD TROUBLE LIFTING THE ADDITIONAL WEIGHT; THESE BARRIERS WERE REMOVED WHEN THE LAKE DROPPED

Glen Canyon Dam was not designed for this eventuality and would be at risk of failing. At the very least, the powerhouse at the base of the dam would be destroyed.

Fortunately, it was Mother Nature who finally solved the problem. On July 15, the water stopped rising, held steady for a few days as all the gates continued to release water at near-maximum capacity, and then the lake level started dropping. The dam had been saved!

Similar problems occurred at Hoover Dam, with Lake Mead's water levels forcing the engineers there to release water through the overflow tunnels. But the damage was less severe at Hoover Dam because the andesite-breccia rock in the canyon walls was much harder and more resistant to erosion than the sandstone at Glen Canyon. Additionally, the overflow tunnels at Hoover were embedded deeper in the canyon walls, which further reduced the risk of erosion reaching back to Lake Mead. Even so, the engineers at Hoover Dam breathed easier knowing they were not going to receive the full volume of Lake Powell because of a breach at Glen Canyon.

PERMANENT REPAIRS

Even with the immediate crisis averted, cavitation was now a known risk that had to be fixed at both dams. Once the regular eight penstocks and four outlet tunnels were capable of handling required water flows, the overflow gates were closed so emergency repair work could begin on the tunnels. Massive amounts of concrete were poured into the damaged tubes to fill the holes the erosion created and to reline the tunnels with smooth concrete. The most important step in the repair process was to notch out an air wedge at the top of the tunnels, particularly at the elbow where the steep tunnel joined the original diversion tunnel. This air wedge was intended to reduce cavitation to a manageable level.

In 1984, when Lake Powell water again rose above the lower edge of the overflow gates, the water was released into the tunnels with little damage. The problem was solved!

Two Decades of Drought

And then it stopped snowing. In the two decades since the floods of 1983–1984, snowfall in the Colorado River basin has been among the lowest in recorded history. Slowly but surely, both Lake Powell and Lake Mead have been drained to provide water to California, Nevada, and Arizona. Lake Mead is now at a historic low and is just two feet above its lowest input level of the penstock tunnels. That means it is very close to the dead-pool level, where water can't be released below the dam. The threat of the reservoir reaching this point is so critical that the city of Las Vegas has spent $817 million to build a new tunnel under the lake. This will be their third "straw" into Lake Mead to make sure they can draw water from the dead pool. If that ever happens, the Colorado

MEN AT WORK CLEARING DEBRIS FROM THE GLEN CANYON DAM OVERFLOW TUNNEL AFTER THE 1983 CRISIS WAS AVERTED

will be bone dry beneath the Hoover Dam, and Southern California and Arizona will be in an obvious water catastrophe.

In response to the current drought, some people believe Lake Powell should be immediately drained to its dead-pool level to raise the level of Lake Mead and reduce the combined evaporative surface of the two reservoirs. Many even call for Glen Canyon Dam to be decommissioned and removed so the river has just one major reservoir instead of two. Of course, many interests reside on both sides of this debate, including those who use Lake Powell for recreation and those who depend on Lake Powell for electricity. Finally, because of the extended drought in other western regions, the upper basin states of Utah, Colorado, and New Mexico are now making claims on Lake Powell water to meet their negotiated share of the diminished flows of the Colorado River. Western water is a complex issue with enormous political, social, and environmental interests and ramifications involved.

At the very least, we know Glen Canyon Dam is secure if high-water years ever return. And we know that four feet of plywood really can save the Grand Canyon!

MEETING THE ENGINEERS WHO SAVED THE DAM

As part of my research for this story, I contacted the Salt Lake office of the Bureau of Reclamation, where Amee Andreason scheduled a visit to the Glen Canyon Dam so I could meet with engineers. She also introduced me to Ginger Reeve, a Bureau graphic-design artist and archivist who helped me select the high-resolution photos included in this chapter.

Along with my good friend Lloyd Kartchner and my brother David, I visited the site on August 25, 2015. What a great experience! Bureau engineers Richard Fehr and Duane Berrier and electrician Chris Mauger met with us, and for two hours, the six of us talked about those frightening days in 1983 when they nearly lost control. Richard and Chris confirmed what I'd been told earlier about red water coming out of the base of the dam. Duane said he didn't remember it that way. All three confirmed that the Bureau knew about the potential problem of cavitation two years earlier than the floods of 1983 because of a similar problem at another dam. But the cost of notching the air wedge was estimated at $5 million in 1981 money, which was not in the budget. And given the low probability of an all-out flood, officials decided to do

U.S. Bureau of Reclamation engineers Chris Mauger and Richard Fehr at Glen Canyon Dam, August 2015

nothing, which resulted in a very expensive mistake because the cost of repairs, including etching the air wedge, was far greater.

Additionally, they discussed how they worried about the overflow gates buckling. Because the gates were radial, bowing in the middle into the lake, the intense force of water coming over the top could cause the gate to buckle. Richard indicated that Bureau projects usually had a safety factor of four, but the overflow gates were built to a safety factor of just one and a half. So adding eight feet to the top of the gates substantially increased the risk of failure. In other words, it was a balancing act to control the flow of water into the tunnels while not overstressing the radial gates. If the gates had buckled, there would have been no control at all.

A final insight I gleaned from our discussion was in regard to the remarkable efforts to rehabilitate the tunnels in the offseason between 1983 and 1984. Richard and Chris attributed this success to Jack Tyler, chief of construction at Glen Canyon Dam, who was brought back to fix the tunnels. Jack and his crew were under incredible time pressure to finish three important tasks:

1. Clean out all the debris. Because the outlets of the overflow tunnels were partially submerged, Jack invented a method whereby a large barge was floated into the base of the tunnel and a cofferdam was built at the entrance to isolate it from the river. Then water was pumped out using submersible pumps lowered into the water. This allowed the barge to settle and the workers to fill it with debris. Once the barge was loaded, the cavern was flooded, and the barge floated downstream to be emptied. They repeated this process many times until they completed the job. It was a huge undertaking Jack managed with skill and ingenuity.

2. Pour more than 2,200 cubic yards of new concrete inside the tunnels to fill the holes the erosion created. All rough surfaces had to be smoothed to reduce cavitations, and the sandstone had to be completely protected by concrete.

3. Cut the air slots in the tunnel using controlled demolition. A business called Controlled Demolition Inc., which invented the practice of imploding obsolete buildings using dynamite, took on the job. They had to use specially placed charges the entire length of the tunnel to cut out the wedge that now prevents cavitations.

The pressure on Jack was intense since floods were expected again in 1984. For Jack to complete such a major renovation in just one season was remarkable. Fortunately his team rose to the challenge.

Concluding thoughts

The conference room in which we were sitting while having this live interview with Richard, Duane, and Chris has floor-to-ceiling windows that overlook Glen Canyon Dam. On the day of our interview, it was calm and serene. The sheer size of the dam is difficult to comprehend without examining it from many angles. Seventy stories of concrete arch is amazing.

The engineers particularly wanted to draw our attention to one of the small miracles of both Glen Canyon Dam and Hoover Dam, which is that they have always delivered the required amount of water to the participating states in the Colorado River Compact. Even after thirteen years of drought, the water continues to flow. Perhaps that's why these men have such a sense of pride in their work. I was personally awed by the humility they displayed in talking about the remarkable job they did two decades ago to save the Glen Canyon Dam.

To me, it is incredible. To them, it was all in a day's work. We are fortunate Richard had the presence of mind to recognize that a stack of plywood lying on the floor of the fabrication plant had the potential to divert a disaster. In doing so, he saved the Grand Canyon.

SOURCES

1. *Glen Canyon Dam and Steel-Arch Bridge.* Stan Jones. Sun Country Publications. Arizona. 1984.

2. *Deadbeat Dams.* Daniel P. Beard. Johnson Books, a Big Earth Publishing Company. Colorado. 2015.

3. "The Summer the Dam Almost Didn't." Roby Morrison. High Country News. June 8, 2010. *Web Exclusive.* http://www.hcn.org/40years/blog/the-summer-the-dam-almost-didnt/ 6/19/2015.

4. "The Year the Dam (Almost) Broke." Philip L. Fradkin. *The Los Angeles Times.* October 29, 1995. http://articles.latimes.com/195-10-29/magazine/tm-62672_1_hoover-dam. 6/19/2015.

5. "Water Vapor Almost Busts Dam." Brian Fortner. *Popular Science.* March 5, 2003. http://www.popsci.com/scitech/article/2003-03/water-vapor-almost-busts-dam. 6/19/2015.

6. "The 1983 Flood in Glen Canyon." Steve Hannon. *Hidden Passage*, Volume 2. *Earthscape.* Summer 1999. http://www.earthscape.org/p2/hp/hp_sum99/hp_sum99a.html.

7. *The Dam Is Not Going to Break.* June 6, 1983. http://jamespowell.org/DeadPool/assets/DeadPoolexcerpt.pdf.

FINAL THOUGHTS

Could history be any more fascinating? People make decisions, and consequences follow. Lee de Forest invented the triode without actually understanding how it worked, and today our world is filled with high-fidelity sound. The men at Glen Canyon Dam recognized the potential in a pile of plywood sheets and saved a billion-dollar dam and many others below it. And the people who pushed for the Teton Dam, in spite of geologists' warnings, paid a heavy price for their mistakes.

Despite my personal connection to the Teton Dam disaster, the story that affected me most was the Halifax explosion. I feel deep empathy for the citizens of Halifax whose lives were shattered because two harbor pilots couldn't agree on how best to pass each other. While all the other stories took years to play out, the Halifax explosion was a mistake measured in minutes that caused suffering for more than seven decades.

History is happening all around us and is most meaningful when we put ourselves into the stories. Hopefully we'll take time to capture the live history we experience either in social media or in a personal journal so our children will have context for the stories that matter most to us.

ABOUT THE AUTHOR

How 4 Feet of Plywood Saved the Grand Canyon is a new approach for Jerry Borrowman, with eight fascinating true stories out of U. S. history that bring the past alive. Jerry is an award-winning, best-selling author of fiction and historical coauthored biographies. He has fifteen books currently in print. To learn more, visit www.jerryborrowman.com.